LEGENDS OF THE RHINE

LEGENDS OF THE RHINE

BY

WILHELM RULAND

WITH ILLUSTRATIONS BY CELEBRATED
ARTISTS

KÖLN AM RHEIN
VERLAG VON HOURSCH & BECHSTEDT

„O, the pride of the German heart is this noble river! And right it is; for of all the rivers of this beautiful earth there is none so beautiful as this."

Longfellow.

The Publishers desire to thank Mr. Andrew Mitchell and Mr. H. J. Findlay, Edinburgh for valuable assistance in the preparation of the new English Edition.

St. Gothard

THE PETRIFIED ALP

In the region where the Rhine has its source there towered in ancient times a green Alp.

This Alp belonged to an honest peasant, and along with a neat little house in the valley below formed his only possession.

The man died suddenly and was deeply mourned by his wife and child. Some days after an unexpected visitor was announced to the widow. He was a man who had much pastureland up in that region, but for a long time his one desire had been to possess the Alp of his neighbour now deceased, as by it his property would be rounded off to his satisfaction.

Quickly making his resolution he declared to the dismayed woman that the Alp belonged to him: her husband had secretly pledged it to him in return for a loan, after the bad harvest of the previous year. When the widow angrily accused him of being an liar the man produced a promissory note, spread it out, and with a hard laugh showed her his statement was confirmed in black

5

and white. The distressed woman burst into tears and declared it was impossible that her late husband should have made a secret transaction of such a nature. The Alp was the sole inheritance of their son, and never would she willingly surrender it.

"I will pay you compensation for the renunciation of your claim, although nothing obliges me to do so", declared the visitor with apparent compassion, in the meantime producing his purse.

The weeping woman motioned to him to put back his gold and told him to go, which he did.

Three days later the widow was summoned before the judge. There the neighbour produced his document and repeated his demand for the possession of the disputed Alp.

The judge, who had been shamefully bribed, declared the document valid and awarded the Alp to the claimant. The broken-hearted widow staggered home.

The new possessor of the Alp on the other hand hastened up to the mountains at full gallop. The man could no longer master his impatience to see for the first time as his legally recognised property the pasture-land he had acquired by deceit.

There, for three days a storm had raged uninterruptedly. As quickly as the soddin paths would permit he ascended to the high country.

Having arrived he stared around with horrified eyes, and fell in a swoon to the earth, overcome with consternation.

Upon the soft green Alp an unseen hand had rolled a mountain of ice. Of the possession which the unjust judge had assigned to him nothing was now to be seen. His own pastures too which adjoined were covered with snow and ice, whilst the meadows of the other Alpine Folk below, lay spread out in the morning light like a velvet carpet.

Towards noon a broken man rode home into the valley cursing himself and the wicked magistrate who had consented to such an evil transaction.

The people there however said to each other: "The Fronfasten Mütterli (the little mother of the Ember-weeks) Frau Sälga passed over our valley last night with her train of maidens. Over the house of that greedy rich man the ghostly company stopped, and by that it is fixed which one must die in the course of the year."

And so it happened. Up there where the youthful Rhine rushes down through deep rocky chasms the petrified Alp stands to this day, a silent warning from bygone days.

THE LAST HOHENRÄTIER

The Domleschg valley was formerly the scene of bitter feuds, and is mentioned in the struggle for freedom by the Swiss peasants of the ancient Bund, some five hundred years ago. There stood the castle of the Hohenrätier.

The last descendant of the degenerate race on the high Realt was rightly feared in the whole district. He was the terror of the peaceful inhabitants of the district, and harried not only them but also merchants and pilgrims who passed along the highway below.

The wrath against this unchivalrous wickedness increased mightily. One day this man perpetrated a daring deed of violence.

Whilst on an excursion into the valley he had discovered a charming maid who sought berries in a lonely wood. In his wicked eagerness he dragged the maiden on to his horse and fled. Amusing himself with her lamentations, he carried his booty up the steep castle hill.

A poacher had observed the occurrence and

alarmed the inhabitants of the village. They carried the news without delay into the Domleschg.

The oppressed people around then rose and joining together approached the castle that very night. Having felled giant trees they threw a bridge over the moat, cast firebrands into the interior, and stormed into the castle-yard through gaps in the gates and walls.

Then the baron appeared mounted on his war-horse, driven out of his abode by tongues of flame.

Before him he held the captured maiden, and in the light of the conflagration his naked sword glittered in his right hand.

Dealing mighty blows on both sides he forced his horse forward (the eyes of which had been bound), intending to make a way down the hill. But the living wall of peasants was impenetrable.

Quickly making his resolution the knight rushed to the side where the wall of rock fell some seven hundred feet sheer into the youthful Rhine.

The foaming steed stood trembling in front of the yawning abyss. The shout of the multitude echoed into the night. Thousands of arms were instantly stretched towards the river and one of them at the last moment succeeded in snatching his prey from the robber, just as the steed tortured and bleeding from sword and spur hurled itself with a mighty spring into the depths below. So ended the last of the Hohenrätiers.

In the dawn only the smoking ruins of the proud castle remained, and the morning bells announced to the peasants that their long desired freedom had been won.

These ruins are situated on the Hinter Rhine above Thusis, and it is said that the last Hohenrätier, like many others of the former tyrants of the Rätigau, yearly on St. John's Eve (when this event occurred) may be seen riding round the fallen walls of his castle, clad in black armour which emits glowing sparks.

*

Basle

ONE HOUR IN ADVANCE

Basle was once surrounded by enemies, and very hard pressed on all sides. A troop of discontented citizens made a shameful compact with the besiegers to help them to conquer the town. It was arranged one dark night that exactly as the clock was striking twelve the attack was to be made from within and without. The traitors were all ready, waiting for midnight in great excitement, having no evil pressentiments of what was about to happen.

The expected hour approached. Accidentally the watchman of the tower heard of the proposed attack, and no time being left to warn the commander of the garrison or the guard, he quickly and with great presence of mind determined upon a safe expedient; he put forward the hand of the great clock one hour, so that instead of striking midnight, the clock struck one.

The traitors in the town looked at each other aghast, believing the enemies outside had neglected or perhaps betrayed them. General doubt and misunderstanding reigned in both camps. While they were debating what plan they must now adopt, the sharp-witted watchman had time to communicate with the magistrate and with the governor of the town. The alarm was raised, the citizens warned, and the treacherous plan comppletely wrecked. The enemy at last, tired of the useless siege, retired discouraged.

The magistrate in remembrance of this remarkable deed ordered that the town-clock should remain in advance as the courageous watchman had set it that eventful night. This singular regulation continued till the year 1798, and although the honest inhabitants of Basle were, as wagging tongues asserted, a century behind-hand in everything else, yet with regard to time they were always one hour in advance.

*

THE TOY OF THE YOUNG
GIANTESS

In olden times a race of giants is said to have
lived in Alsace. Castle Niedeck in the valley of
the Breusch was their residence, but even the ruins
of this fortress have long since disappeared. The
legend however remains to tell us that they were
a peaceable people, welldisposed to mankind.

The daughter of the owner of the castle was one
day taking a leisurely walk through the adjoining
wood. On approaching the fields and meadows
of the valley, she perceived a peasant ploughing.
The young giantess looked in great astonishment
at the tiny man who seemed to be so busily
engaged trudging along after his little team, and
turning up the ground with his small iron instrument. She had never beforde seen anything so
wonderful, and was very much amused at the
sight.

It seemed to her a nice little toy, and she
clapped her hands in childish glee, so that the
echo sounded among the mountains; then pick-

ing up man, horse, and plough, she placed them in her apron and hurried back gaily to the castle. There she showed her father the nice little toy, greatly pleased at what she had found.

The giant however shook his enormous head gravely, and said in a displeased tone, "Don't you know, child, who this trembling little creature with his struggling tiny animal is, that you have chosen for a plaything? Of all the dwarfs down in the valley below, he is the most useful; he works hard and indefatigably in scorching heat as well as in cold and windy weather, so that the fields may produce fruit for us. He who scoffs at or maltreats him will be punished by Heaven. Take the little labourer therefore back to the place he came from."

The young giantess, greatly ashamed and blushing deeply with embarrassment, put the amusing little toy back into her apron, and carried it obediently down to the valley.

*

THE CATHEDRAL CLOCK

The Cathedral was finished, and the city magistrates resolved to place an ingenious clock on the upper tower. For al long time they searched in vain, but at last a master was found who offered to create a work of art such as had never been seen in any land. The members of the council were highly satisfied with this proposal, and the master began his work.

Weeks and months passed, and when at last it was finished there was general astonishment; the clock was indeed so wonderful that nothing to match it could be found in the whole country. It marked not only the hours but the days and months as well; a globe was attached to it which also marked out the rising and the setting of the sun, and the eclipses of that body and the moon could be seen at the very moment when they took place in nature. Every change was pointed out by Mercury's wand, and every constellation appeared at the right time. Shortly before the stroke of the clock a figure representing Death emerged from the centre and sounded the full hour, while at the quarter and half hours the statue of Christ came forth, repelling the destroyer of all life. Added to all these wonders was a beautiful chime that played melodious hymns.

Such was the marvellous clock in the cathedral of Strassbourg. The magistrates however proved themselves unworthy of their new possession; pride and presumption got the better of them, making them commit a most unjust and ungrateful action.

They desired their town to be the only one in the land which possessed such a work of art, and in order to prevent the maker from making another like it, they did not shrink from the vilest of crimes.

Taking advantage of the rumour that such a wonderful work could only have been made by the aid of witchcraft, the accused the clock-maker of being united with the devil, threw him into prison, and cruelly condemned him to be blinded. The unhappy artist resigned himself to his bitter fate without a murmur. The only favour he asked was that he might be allowed to examine the clock once again before the judgment was carried out. He said he wanted to arrange something in the works which no one else could understand.

The crafty magistrates, being anxious to have the clock perfect, granted him this request.

The artist filed, sawed, regulated here and there, and then was led away, and in the same hour deprived of his sight.

The cruel deed was hardly accomplished, when it was found that the clock had stopped. The artist had destroyed his work with his own hands; his righteous determination that the chimes would never ring again, had become a melancholy truth. Up to the present no one has been able again to set the dead works going. An equally splendid clock now adorns the cathedral, but the remains of the first one have been preserved ever since.

*

Worms

THE NIBELUNGEN LIED

To-day we are deeply touched, as our fore-fathers must have been at the recital of the boundless suffering and the overwhelming concatenation of sin and expiation in the lives of the Recken and Frauen of the Nibelungen Legend. That naive singer has remained nameless and unknown, who about the end of the 12th century wrote down this legend in poetic form, thus preserving forever our most precious relic of Germanic Folksepic. A powerful story it is of sin and suffering: corresponding to the world itself and just as the primitive mind of a people loves to represent it. The story begins as a lovely idyll but ends in gloomy tragedy.

The ancient Rhenish town of Worms was during the great migrations the seat of authority of the Burgundian invaders, an east Germanic stock. During the glorious reign of King Gunther there appears, attracted by the beauty of Chriemhild the king's sister, a young hero, Siegfried, by name. He is himself a king's son, his father Siegmund reigning in Xanten „nieden by dem Rine". King Gunther receives the fair Recken into his service as a vassal.

Siegfried, exhibiting the fairest loyalty to his overlord, and rendered invisible by magic, conquers for him the redoubtable Brunhild, the proud queen of the island kingdom of Isenland (Iceland) and compels her to wed King Gunther. As a reward Siegfried receives the hand of Chriemhild. In the fulness of his heart the hero presents to Chriemhild as a marriage gift, the Nibelungen Hoard, which he had acquired in his early years from the sons of the king of the Nibelungen and from Dwarf Alberich the guardian of the treasure.

Joy reigns in the king's court at Worms, but it was not shared by all. Besides Chriemhild there was another secretly drawn towards the hero, and in Brunhild's heart the bridal happiness of Chriemhild awakens such envy that soon no friendly word passes between the women. They become estranged and one day her bad feeling leads Brunhild to harsh words. Then alas, Chriemhild gave unbridled licence to her tongue. In her rash insolence she represents to Brunhild that it was not Gunther but Siegfried who formerly overcame her. As proof of this she produces the ring and girdle which Siegfried had

taken on that night from the powerful Brunhild, and which he had presented to Chriemhild. With fierce haughtiness Chriemhild taunts her opponent with a hateful name no woman could endure, and forbids her to enter the cathedral.

Brunhild, weeping, informs King Gunther of the contumely heaped upon her. The king is filled with wrath, and his vassal, the gloomy Hagen considers how he may destroy Siegfried ostensibly to avenge the Queen, but secretly for the possession of the Nibelungen Hoard. During a hunt in the Odenwald Siegfried was treacherously stabbed by Hagen whilst stooping to drink from a well. The intention was to spread the report that Siegfried had been slain by robbers whilst hunting alone. So, on the following day they crossed the Rhine back to Worms.

In the night Hagen caused the dead body of Siegfried to be laid in front of Chriemhild's chamber. In the early morning as Chriemhild accompanied by her attendants was preparing to go to mass in the cathedral she noticed the corpse of her hero. A wail of sorrow arose. Chriemhild threw herself weeping on the body of her murdered husband. "Alas!" she cried "thy shield is not hacked by swords: thou hast been foully murdered. Did I but know who has done this, I would avenge thy death". Chriemhild ordered a magnificent bier for her royal hero, and demanded that an ordeal should be held over the corpse. "For it is a marvellous thing, and to this day it happens, that when the bloodstained murderer approaches wounds bleed anew".

So all the princes and nobles of Burgundy walked past the dead body, above which was the figure of the crucified Redeemer of the world, and lo! when the grim Hagen came forward the wounds of the dead man began to flow. In the presence of the astounded men and horrified women Chriemhild accused Hagen of the assassination of her husband.

Much treachery and woe accompanied the expiation of this great crime. The Nibelungen Hoard, the cause of the shameful deed, was sunk in the middle of the Rhine in order to prevent future strife arising from human greed. But Chriemhild's undying sorrow was not mitigated, nor her unconquerable thirst for revenge appeased.

After the burial of his son King Siegmund begged in vain that Chriemhild should come to the royal city of Xanten; she remained at Worms for thirteen years constantly near her dead beloved.

Then the sorrowing woman removed to the Abbey of Lorch which her mother, Frau Ute, had founded. Thither also, she transferred Siegfried's body.

When Etzel (Attila) the ruler of the Huns wooed her, Chriemhild urged not by love but by very different feelings gave him her hand and accompanied her heathen lord to the land of the Magyars. Then she treacherously invited Siegfried's murderers to visit her husband, and prepared for them a destruction which fills the mind with horror. The Burgundian king and his followers, who, since the Hoard had come into their possession, were called the Nibelungen, fell slaughtered in the Etzelburg under the swords of the Huns and their allies, thus atoning for their faithlessness to the hero Siegfried. And with this awful holocaust ends the Lied of the Nibelungen Not, the most renowned heroic legend in the German tongue.

Speyer

THE BELLS OF SPEYER

The German Emperor, Henry IV, had much trouble to bear under his purple mantle. Through his own and through stranger's faults the crown which he wore was set with thorns, and even into the bosom of his family this unhappy spirit of dissension had crept. The excommunication by the Pope, his powerful enemy, was followed by the revolt of the princes, and lastly by the conspiracy of his own sons. His eldest son, Conrad, openly rebelled against him, and treated his father most contemptuously. When this prince died suddenly, the second son, Henry, attempted the deposition of his father and made intrigues against him. Thus forced to abdicate his throne the broken-down emperor fled to Liège, accompanied by one faithful servant, Kurt, and there lay down to his last rest.

His body was left for five years in unconsecrated ground in a foreign country. Kurt remained faithful, and prayed incessantly at the burial-place of his royal master.

At last the Pope at Henry's request consented to recall the ban. Henry ordered his father's remains to be brought to Speyer and solemnly interred with the royal family. Kurt was allowed to follow the procession to Speyer, but wearied out by this long watching the old man died a few days afterwards. Just at the moment of his death the bells in the cathedral at Speyer tolled without any human hand putting them in motion, as they always did when an imperial death took place.

Years passed.

The German emperor Henry V. lay dying on his luxurious couch at Speyer. His bodily sufferings were intense, but the agony of his mind was even greater; he had obtained the crown which now pressed so heavily on his head, by shameful treacherous means. The apparition of his father dying in misery appeared to him, and no words of the flatterers at his bed-side could still the voice of his conscience. At last death freed him from all his torments, and at the same hour the bells which were always rung when a poor sinner was led to execution, tolled, set in motion by no human hand.

Thus were the bells the instrument of that Hand which wisely and warningly wrote . . . . "Honour thy father and thy mother . . ."

THE KNAVE OF BERGEN

The emperor was to be crowned at Frankfort and great festivities were to be given in the town in his honour, among them a masquerade, at which knights and noble ladies rivalled each other in splendour. Joy was depicted on every face at this great assembly, only one knight among the many guests being noticeable for his gravity and restraint. He wore black armour, and the feather waving above his visor was black too. No one knew him or could guess who he was. He approached the empress with a noble grace, bent his knee, and asked her to dance with him, which she graciously consented to do. He glided gracefully through the splendid halls with the queen of the festival, and soon every eye was turned on them, and everyone was eager to know who he was.

The empress was charmed with her excellent partner, and the grace of his refined conversation pleased her so much that she granted him a second and a third dance.

Everyone became more and more curious to know who this masked knight was. Meanwhile the hour struck when every mask had to be raised, and every masked guest must make himself known. More than all the others the empress was anxious to know who her partner was. But he hesitated and even refused to take off his mask until she ordered him peremptorily to do so. The knight obeyed, but none of the high ladies or noble knights recognised him. Suddenly two stewards pressed through the crowd, crying out with indignation and horror;

"It is the headsman from Bergen!"

Then the emperor in great wrath ordered the shameful offender who had thus degraded the empress and insulted his sovereign to be led to execution.

But the culprit, throwing himself at the emperor's feet, said holdly, "I have transgressed, my lord, and offended you and your noble guests, but most heavily have I sinned against my queen. No punishment, not even blood, will be able to wash out the disgrace you have suffered through me. Therefore, oh King! allow me to propose a remedy to efface the shame. Draw you sword and knight me, and I will throw down my gauntlet to any one who dares to speak disrespectfully of my sovereign."

The emperor was taken by surprise at this bold proposal. However it appeared the wisest plan to adopt.

"You are a knave," he replied after a moment's consideration, "but your advice is good and displays prudence, just as your offence shows adventurous courage. Well then," — laying his sword on the man's neck — "rise Sir Knight. You have acted like a knave, and the Knave of Bergen you shall be called henceforth."

A joyful shout of approbation pealed through the halls, and the new knight again glided gracefully through the crowd with the queen of the festival.

*

HEINRICH FRAUENLOB

The priest or as some say, canon, in the old town of Mayence was a very worthy man, and at the same time a heaven-gifted singer. Besides devoting himself to science, he composed numerous pious verses which he dedicated to the Holy Virgin. He also played the harp, and wrote many beautiful songs in honour of the female sex.

In contrast to many contemporary poets, he considered "woman" a higher title than "wife" which only signifies a married woman. So on account of the chivalry displayed in his numberless poems and songs, posterity gave him the name of "Frauenlob", under which title he is better known than under his own name of Heinrich of Meissen.

The love and veneration which thankful women paid him was very great, not only during his life-time, but even more so after his death. Their grief was intense when it became known that the poet's voice would never more be heard

in this world. It was agreed to honour him with such a burial as no poet had ever before received. The funeral procession moved slowly and sorrowfully along the streets, the greater part of the cortege being women in deep mourning who prayed for the repose of the poet's soul. Eight of the most beautiful among them carried the coffin, which was covered with sweet-scented flowers.

At the grave songs of lamentation were heard from women's gentle voices. Precious Rhine-wine which had been the poet's favourite drink, and which so often had inspired his poetry, was poured by the hands of his admirers over his grave, so profusely, the legend relates, that the entrance of the church was flooded by the libation. But still more precious than all these gifts were the tears, which on this memorable day were shed by many a gentle lady.

The wanderer can still see the monument erected to this great benefactor in the cathedral at Mayence, which represents the figure of a beautiful woman in pure white marble placing a wreath on the coffin of the great singer, who had honoured women in the most chivalrous of songs.

JOHANNISBERG

Wherever the German tongue is heard, and even further still, the king of all Rhine wines, "Johannisberger" is known and sought after. Every friend of the grape which grows on the banks of this river is well acquainted with it, but few perhaps know of its princely origin. It is princely, not because princes' hands once kept the key to Johannisberg, but rather because princely hands planted the vine in the Rhine country, and this royal giver was no other than Charlemagne, the all-powerful ruler of the kingdom of the Franks.

Once in early spring Charles the Great was standing on the balcony of his castle at Ingelheim, his eyes straying over the beautiful stretch of country at his feet. Snow had fallen during the night, and the hills of Rüdesheim were clothed in white. As the imperial ruler was looking thoughtfully over the landscape, he noticed that the snow on one side of Johannisberg melted quicker in the sun's rays than on any other part. Charles, who was a great and deep thinker, began to reflect that on a spot where the rays of the sun shone so genially, something better than grass would thrive.

Sending for Kunrat his faithful servant, he bade him saddle his horse the next day at dawn and ride to Orleans, a town famous for its good wine. He was to inform the citizens that the emperor had not forgotten the excellent wine they had given him there, and that he would like to grow the same vines on the Rhine. He desired the citizens of Orleans therefore to send him plants from their country.

The messenger set off to do the king's bidding and ere the moon had again gone round her course, was back in the castle at Ingelheim. Great satisfaction prevailed at court. Charles, mighty ruler as he was, even went so far as to cross to Rüdesheim, where he planted with his royal hand the French vine in German soil.

This was no mere passing whim on the part of the emperor. He sent messengers constantly to bring word how the vines were thriving in Rüdesheim and on the flanks of Johannisberg, and when the third autumn had come round, the Emperor Charlemagne set out from his favourite resort, Aix-la-Chapelle, for the Rhine country, and great rejoicing prevailed among the vine-reapers from Rüdesheim to Johannisberg.

The first cup of wine was solemnly offered to the emperor, a golden wine in a golden goblet, a wine worthy of a king.

Charles took a long deep draught, and with brightened eyes praised the delicious drink. It became his favourite wine, this fiery "Johannisberger", making him young again in his old age. What Charlemagne then felt when he drank this wine, every one who raises the sparkling grape-juice to his lips is keenly sensible of also. Wherever the German tongue is heard, and even further still, the king of all Rhine wines is known and sought after, Johannisberger wine.

———

The legend weaves another wonderful tale about the great emperor's blessing his grapes.

A poet's pen has fashioned it into a song, which is still often heard among the grape-gatherers.

Every spring when the vines are blossoming on the hills and in the valleys along the river, and their fragrance scents the air, a tall shadow wanders about the vineyards at night, a purple mantle hanging from his stately shoulders, and a crown on his head. It is Charlemagne, the great Emperor, who planted the grapes long years before. The luscious scent of the blossoms wakens him up from his tomb in Aix-la-Chapelle, and he comes to bless the grapes.

When the full moon gently casts her bright beams on the water, lighting up the emperor's nightly path, he may be seen crossing the golden bridge formed by her rays and then wandering further along the hills, blessing the vines on the other side of the river.

At the first crow of the cock he returns to his grave in Aix-la-Chapelle, and sleeps till the scent of the grapes wakens him next spring, when be again wanders through the countries along the Rhine, blessing the vineyards.

———

Let us now relate another little story which is told of the monks who lived at Johannisberg.

Once the high Abbot of Fulda came unexpectedly to visit the cloister at Johannisberg just about the time when the grapes were ripe. The worthy Abbot made many inquiries about his people, showed himself highly pleased with the works of the industrious monks, and as a mark of his continued favour, invited all the inmates of the cloister to a drinking bout.

"Wine maketh the heard glad," thus quoting King David's significant words, the holy man began his speech: "God's loving hand will be

gracious in future years to your vines. Let us profit by his grace, brothers, and drink what he has provided for us in moderation and with reverence. But before we refresh ourselves with God's good gifts, take your breviaries and let us begin with a short prayer.

"Breviaries!" was whispered along the rows, and the eyes in the fat genial faces blinked in helpless embarrassment.

"Yes, your breviaries," and the white-haired Abbot looked silently but sternly at the brothers.

They searched and searched.

Gradually the frown disappeared from the Abbot's face, and a smile gradually spread over his withered features.

"Well, never mind, let us drink," said he. Then feeling his pockets, he said with a gleam in his eye, 'That's too bad! I ought to have the Rhine."

A corkscrew! Every one plunges his hand into his pocket, and as many corkscrews were produced before the worthy Abbot as there were brothers present.

Then a gleam of merriment beamed in the Abbot's eyes.

"Bravo, ye pious monks! what a plentiful supply of corkscrews! Do not all look so embarrassed, we shall not be annoyed about it to-day but — to-morrow! Now we shall sing with King David. "Wine maketh the heart glad,"" and the uncorked bottle went the rounds.

EGINHARD AND EMMA

I.

The story which we have now to relate is a very touching one, and it becomes even more interesting when we know that it is based on real fact.

In the little town of Ingelheim there was a beautiful marble castle, the favourite residence of Charlemagne. He often retired to this lonely, peaceful spot accompanied only by a few of his faithful vassals and the members of his own family. Eginhard, the emperor's private secretary, was never missing from this little circle. Charlemagne thought highly of this man, then in the prime of youth, on account of his profound knowledge and extraordinary talents.

The young scholar, so different from the wise councillors not only in his learning but in his cultivated manners, was a great favourite among the ladies of the court.

Eginhard who was a constant companion of the emperor, had also become an intimate member of the family circle, and Charlemagne entrusted him with the education of his favourite child Emma, daughter of his wife Gismonda. This dark-eyed maiden was considered the most beautiful of her age, and the young scholar could not long remain cold and indifferent to her charms. The undisturbed hours which should have been spent in learning, led to a mutual understanding. Eginhard struggled to remind himself of his duty towards his sovereign, but love overcame him, and soon an oath of eternal fidelity united these young hearts.

II.

The great emperor ought to have known what would be the consequence of allowing the young scholar to enjoy the society of his dark-eyed, passionate daughter. In the still hours of the night when all the inmates of the castle lay wrapped in sleep, Eginhard sought the chamber of his beloved. She listened enchanted to the glowing words of his burning heart, but their love was chaste and pure, no gusts of passion troubling them.

But fate was against these lovers. One night they were sitting in Emma's chamber in mutual exchange of confidence. The great palace was veiled in darkness, no ray of light, no star was to be seen in the heavens. As Eginhard was about to leave the chamber, he perceived that the courtyard below was covered with snow. It would be impossible to pass across it without leaving traces behind him, but at all risks he must reach his room.

What was to be done? Love is ingenious. After considering for some time together, they both concluded that there was but one way to prevent their being discovered. The slender maiden took her lover on her back and carried him across the courtyard, thus leaving behind only her small foot-prints.

It happened that Charles the Great had not yet sought the repose he needed so much, as care banished sleep from his eyes. He sat at his window and looked out into the silent night. In the courtyard below he perceived a shadow crossing the pavement and, looking carefully, he recognised his favourite daughter Emma carrying a man on her back. — Yes! and this man was Eginhard his great favourite. Pain and anger struggled in his heart. He wanted to rush down and kill him — an emperor's daughter and a mere secretary — but with a great effort he restrained himself, mastered the violent agitation which this unexpected sight caused him, and went back to his chamber to wait wearily for dawn.

III.

The next day Charles assembled his councillors. They were all horrified to see his ghastly look; his brow was dark, and sorrow was printed on every feature. Eginhard looked at his master, apprehending coming evil. Charlemagne stood up and spoke: —

"What does a royal princess deserve, who receives the visit of a man at night?" The councillors looked at each other speechless. Eginhard's countenance became white as death. The councillors soon guessed the name of the royal princess, and they consulted together for some time not knowing what to say, but at last one councillor answered: —

"Your Majesty, we think that a weak woman must not be punished for anything done out of love."

"And what does a favourite of the emperor deserve who creeps into a royal princess' chamber at night?"

Charlemagne cast a dark look at his secretary, who trembled and became even paler. "Alas! all is lost," murmured he to himself. Then, raising his voice, he said, "Death, my Master and Emperor!"

Charles looked at the young man full of astonishment. The wrath in his soul melted at this self-condemnation and fervent repentance. Deep silence followed this answer, and in a few minutes the emperor dismissed his councillors, making a sign at the same time to Eginhard to follow him.

Without a word Charles led him into his private chamber, where in answer to his summons, Emma appeared.

Her heart failed her as she saw the dark look on her father's face and the troubled features of her beloved. She understood all at once, and with a convulsive cry of pain threw herself at her father's feet.

"Mercy! mercy! my father, we love each other so dearly!" she murmured, raising her large eyes imploringly. "Mercy!" murmured Eginhard too, bending his knees.

The emperor remained silent. After a time he began to speak earnestly and coldly at first, but his voice changed to a milder tone on hearing the sobs of his favourite child.

"I shall not separate you who are bound to each other by love. A priest shall unite you, and at dawn to-morrow you must both be gone from the castle, never to return."

He left them, shutting the door behind him.

The beautiful maiden sank down on her knees, only half conscious in her grief of what

her father had said. But Eginhard's soft voice soon whispered in her ear.

"Do not weep, Emma. By thrusting you from him, your father, my master, has only bound us together for ever. Come," he continued in a trembling voice, alarmed at her passionate tears, "we must go, but love will be ever with us."

The next day two pilgrims left the castle of Ingelheim, and took the road in the direction of Mayence.

IV.

Time wore on.

Charles the Great had made war on Saxony, had set the Roman crown upon his own head, and had become famous throughout the whole world. But all his fame had not prevented his hair from becoming grey, no his heart from being sad. A mournful picture had imprinted itself on his mind, despite all his efforts to forget the past. In the evening when the setting sun glittered on the marble pillars of the royal palace, casting its golden rays into the chamber of the great emperor, it would find him sitting motionless in his carved oak-chair, his grey head buried in his hands, mournful dreams troubling his peace. He was thinking of the days which were past, of the young man whose gentle ways made him so different from the rough warriors of the court, how he used to recite poetry and sing the songs of the old bards so passionately, and the old legends which the emperor prized so much, how he used to read to him from the old gray parchment which he, Eginhard, had written so carefully, how his own favourite, dark-eyed daughter had so often been present, sitting at his feet listening intently to the reader — all this came back to his meinory, saddening his heart, and filling his eyes with tears.

V.

Bugle-horns sounded through the forest, Charles and his followers were at the chase. The old emperor, seeking to forget his grief, had seized his spear and had gone out to hunt.

In his eagerness to follow a magnificent stag he had become separated from his escort. The sun was already low in the west; the animal, now seeing no way of escape, as his pursuer was close behind him, dashed into a river and swam to the other side. The emperor, in hot pursuit and much exhausted, arrived at the water's edge, and for the first time noticed that he was alone, and in a part of the country quite unknown to him.

The river lay before him and the forest behind, but the latter seemed to be quite impenetrable. It was already night, and Charles sought in vain to find some path or track.

As he was looking round him, he perceived a light in the distance. Greatly pleased he started off in that direction, and found a little hut close to the river, but on looking through the window Charlemagne saw that the room was a very poor one.

"Perhaps this is the hermitage of some pious man," thought he, and knocked at the door, whereupon a fair haired man appeared on the threshold.

Without mentioning his name, the emperor informed him of what had happened, and begged shelter for the night.

At the sound of this loved voice, the man trembled, but controlling himself, he invited the emperor to enter. A young woman was sitting on a stool rocking a baby in her arms. She started, became very pale at the sight of the emperor, and then hurried into the next room to hide her emotion; Charles sat down, and refusing refreshment from his host leaned his head wearily on his hands.

Minutes passed, and still he sat there lost in thought, dreaming of those happy by-gone days.

At last the sweet prattle of a child roused

him, and looking up he saw a little girl about five years old at his side, stretching out her arms to him, bidding him good-night. Charles looked closely at the little angel-like creature, his heart throbbing within him. "What is your name, little one?" asked he. "Emma," answered the child.

"Emma," repeated Charles with tears in his eyes, and drawing the child closer to him he pressed a kiss on its forehead.

In a moment the man and his young wife were at the emperor's feet imploring pardon. "Emma! Eginhard!" cried he with great emotion, embracing them both. "Blessed be the place where I have found you again!"

Emma and Eginhard returned in great pomp to the emperor's court. The latter gave them his beautiful palace at Ingelheim, and only felt himself happy when he was with them.

He caused a cloister to be built on the spot where he had found them again, which to the present day is called "Seligenstadt," "town of the happy."

In the church belonging to this little town the tomb of Eginhard and Emma is still shown, for according to their wishes, their bones were interred in the same coffin.

THE BRÖMSERBURG

In the lofty cathedral of Spires stood a great assemblage of knights, and on the throne near the altar sat Conrad der Staufe with his hands resting on the hilt of his sword. All were listening intently to the burning words of Bernard of Clairvaux who was describing the ruthless manner in which the holy places of Palestine had been laid waste. As the saintly preacher ended with a thrilling appeal to the religious feelings of his audience, a great shout, "On, to Jerusalem!" rang through the sacred edifice. Most of the knights offered to bring as many followers as possible to aid their pious Emperor. Among those present was Hans Brömser, the lord of the Niederburg at Rüdesheim. This noble knight, the last of his race, was not detained at home by family cares. His wife had early been taken from him by death, and Mechtildis, the only offspring of their marriage, was left under the protection of the neighbouring Falkenstein family.

So the pious warriors marched by devious and

dangerous routes to that land where Our Lord lived and suffered. In fierce battle with the Saracens many a noble knight closed his eyes forever. Many met a harder fate — a living death in the noisome prisons of the unbelievers. After a lost battle Sir Brömser fell into the hands of the Turks, and in a dungeon had to suffer shameful imprisonment. Sometimes they would force their knightly foe to turn a millstone, while the crowd jeered. Then, in the hour of deepest misery the knight made a vow to God. "Give me my freedom again, and I vow that my child Mechtildis shall devote her life to the Church." And he repeated the solemn words again, and yet a third time.

Then happened what none of his companions in-arms had ever hoped for. The brave crusaders stormed this Turkish stronghold in the Syrian desert, and liberated their fellow-crusaders from captivity. Full of gratitude to God, Hans Brömser again fought valiantly in the holy cause.

Meanwhile at home in the hospitable keep above the Rhine a maiden awaited with anxiety the return of her father. Often in the silent hours, with sweetness and sunshine around her, without and within, she stood on the castle-wall and she saw in reverie that blue Eastern land, whilst she listened, to the wild throbbing of her young heart in which the blossoms of first love were bursting.

Then one night her father returned to the Rhineland.

In the moss-covered courtyard of the castle Mechtildis embraced her father long and silently. Beside the maiden, now in her seventeenth year, stood the young lord of Falkenstein. The youth bowed deeply to the lord of the Brömserburg, and greeted him kindly with the words, "Welcome home, father!" Then the vow made in the Syrian prison rose like a spectre to pall the joy of the crusader's ruturn.

In the banqueting hall of the castle a large company had assembled to celebrate the happy return of Hans Brömser and his faithful companions. The praise of the crusaders resounded and many stories were told of the dangers the heroes had encountered. With stirring words the knight related to his listening guests how he himself had fought in the sacred cause, and how he had suffered imprisonment among the heathen. Then in a lower tone, and with solemn words, he told his friends of the vow he had made in his hour of deep despair in the Syrian dungeon.

The painful silence which followed was broken by a stifled cry, and the knight's daughter, pale as the covering on the festive board, sank unconscious to the floor. With burning cheek and flashing eye the young lord of Falkenstein rose, and with a firm voice exclaimed, "Mechtildis belongs to me; she has solemnly given herself to me forever". The murmur soon subsided before the stern countenance of the lord of the castle. "Mechtildis has been dedicated to heaven, not to you, boy. The last of the Brömser race has sworn it, and abides by it". The knight said this with suppressed fury, and soon his guests departed in silence.

Mechtildis lay in her chamber in wild grief. The flickering lamp beside the crucifix threw an unsteady light on the extended form of the maiden who was measuring the tedious night hours in the love-anguish of her young heart. To the distracted maid her chamber seemed to be transformed into an oppressive dungeon. Seizing the lamp with a trembling hand she hurried up the narrow winding stair on to the roof of the castle, and there confided her great grief to the listening ear of night. Leaning on the wall, she looked away towards the castle where lived the noble young lord to whom she had dedicated her life. "I am thine, my beloved," she sobbed. No star was visible in the sky. A wild autumn wind shrieked and swirled round the keep in accompaniment to the storm in the maiden's breast. A short piercing cry echoed in the darkness. Was it the bride of the winds or a human cry? The night swallowed it. From the parapet of the Brömserburg a female form had been hurled down into the dark floods of the Rhine below.

A bright harvest morning followed a stormy night. In the Brömserburg they were searching everywhere in vain for their lord's daughter. Soon however a mournful procession approached bearing the mortal remains of Mechtildis. In the early dawn a young woman had rescued the body from the waters of the river. Now the walls of the Brömserburg echoed with sounds of woe over the early death of this last fair young flower of the Brömser race. Hans Brömser threw himself on the body and buried his stern features in the snowy linen. Not a tear bedewed his eyelids.

As a propitiatory offering for the repose of the soul of the maiden who had thus avoided the monastic life, the knight in his deep sorrow vowed to build a chapel on the hill opposite his castle. Then Hans Brömser shut himself up in his chamber, and passed the following days in silent grief, while the grave closed over his wretched child.

Many months passed, but still not a stone of the promised chapel had been set up. In the bitterness of his sorrow the grief-stricken father had separated himself more and more from the world, and now brooded in gloomy isolation. One day a servant came before him with a likeness of the Mother of God which an ox had scraped up while ploughing a field on the hill opposite the castle, and three times the servant declared he had heard the "Not Gottes" (Suffering of God) called out. Then Hans Brömser remembered his vow, and the chapel for the peace of the soul of Mechtildis was erected. "Not Gottes" it is called to this day.

*

THE MOUSE-TOWER

Below Bingen in the middle of the Rhine there is a lonely island on which a stronghold is to be seen. This tower is called "the Mouse-Tower". For many centuries a very gloomy tale has been told about it in connection with Hatto, Archbishop of Mayence, whose evil deeds were well-known throughout the country.

Hatto is said to have been ambitious, heartless, and perfidious, as well as cruel towards the poor. He extorted taxes from his people, tolls were imposed, and new burdens invented only to gratify his haughty pride and his love of display. On a little island between Bingen and Rüdesheim he caused a tower to be built, so that all passing ships could be stopped in the narrow passage, where they were obliged to pay toll.

Soon after the building of this custom-house there was a very bad harvest in the country round Mayence. Drought had parched the fields, and the little seed remaining had been destroyed by hail. The scarcity was felt all the more, because the bishop had bought up all the stores of corn that were left from the year before, and had stored them up safely in his granaries.

A terrible famine now threatened the land, spreading misery among the poor. The unhappy people implored the cruel bishop to lower the price of the corn in his store-house, which he wished to sell at such exorbitant prices that his subjects could not buy it. All their petitions were in vain. His advisers besought him to have pity on the deplorable condition of the poor, but Hatto remained unmoved. When cries of distress and the murmuring voices of the exasperated folk were raised against their hard-hearted master, the bishop gave free vent to the wicked thoughts of his soul.

One day a troop of hungry beggars came crowding to the episcopal palace crying for food. Hatto and his guests were just sitting down to a luxurious banquet. The bishop had been talking to his companions of these wretched people, and had expressed his opinion that it would be a good thing to do away with them altogether in some drastic way.

As the ragged mob of men, women, and children, with hollow cheeks and pale faces threw themselves at his feet crying for bread, a still more fiendish plan suggested itself. Beckoning to them with hypocritical kindness he promised them corn, and caused them to be led outside the town to a barn, where each one was to receive as much corn as he wished. The unhappy folk hurried forth, their hearts full of gratitude; but when they were all in the barn, Hatto ordered the doors to be locked and the barn to be set on fire.

The screams of the poor wretches were heart-rending, and could be heard even in the bishop's palace.

But cruel Hatto called out scornfully to his advisers, "Listen! how the mice are squeaking among the corn. This eternal begging is at an end at last. May the mice bite me if it is not true!"

But the punishment which Heaven sent him was terrible. Thousands of mice came out of the burning barn, made their way to the palace, filled every chamber and corner, and at last attacked the bishop himself. His servants killed them by hundreds, but their numbers seemed only to increase, as did their ferocity also. The bishop was seized with horror and, anticipating God's punishment, he fled from the town and went on board a boat hoping to defend himself from his terrible pursuers. But the innumerable horde

swam in legions after him, and when he reached his tower on the island thinking at least he would be safe there, the mice followed him, gnawing the tower and tearing for themselves an entrance with their sharp teeth, till at last they reached him whom they sought. The cruel man was devoured by the mice, which attacked him in scores. In his despair he offered his soul to the Evil One, if he would release his body from such awful agony. The Evil Spirit came, freed his body, but took his soul away for himself.

Thus runs the legend. History however speaks less severely of Hatto, the imperious prelate.

———

His great ambition was his desire for power. He was the founder of the temporal power which the seat of Mayence obtained, and which later on made it the first bishopric of the kingdom, but he was always hated by the citizens, who suffered much owing to his proud, despotic character.

It is true that he was the founder of the toll which ships in olden times were obliged to pay on the Rhine, so that this fact and many other cruel exactions of his, have helped to evolve the terrible legend of the Mouse-Tower.

The Valley of the Nahe
Kreuznach

A MIGHTY DRAUGHT

Once upon a time in the high castle called Rheingrafenstein near Kreuznach, the flower of the knights belonging to the Rhine country were assembled.

They were powerful warriors, these nobles of ancient rank, but the most prominent among them was the host himself, the proud Count of the Rhine. Many a cup had he already emptied to the health of his distinguished guests, and rising up once more from his richly carved chair he cast a look over the brilliant assembly and said in a boastful tone.

"I have got a knight's high boot here, my noble lords. A courier left it behind him once. Now I promise on the honour of my house that whoever will drink it empty at one draught, to hime I will give the village of Hüffelsheim yonder."

The count, smiling at the novelty of the challenge, took the boot from his attendant's hand, caused it to be filled to the brim, and held up this novel cup to his guests. "This a fair challenge! Come on whoever will dare!" said he.

Among the illustrious company present there was one, John of Sponheim, a knight well-known in the country for his enormous drinking powers; but he remained unmoved at these defiant words, only looking inquiringly at his neighbour, Knight Weinhart of Dhaun, who in great perplexity, was striving to hide his head behind a large goblet. Old Flörsheimer, another knight whose thirst usually seemed unquenchable, stroked his gray beard doubtfully, while Kunz of Stromberg, a tall thin man, shook his head at the through of the after-effects which such a draught would bring. Even the chaplain of the castle, who attributed his effective intoning of high-mass to the virtues of the Rhenish wine which he indulged in so freely, looked longingly at the boot, but had not the courage to attempt such a rash act.

Suddenly a knight, Boss of Waldeck by name, rose. He was a muscular man with the strength of a bear. Banging his mighty first upon the table, he thurdered scornfully: "Bring me that little boot!"

The distinguished company stared at him in great astonishment, but Boos of Waldeck, taking the boot in his sturdy fist, cried out. "Your health, my lords!"

Then flourishing it in the air, he emptied the boot at one draught.

When this act was accomplished, Boos threw himself heavily into his chair, and addressing the master of the ceremonies, said with a humorous twinkle in his eye:

"Did the courier not leave the other boot too? I might possibly win a second bet, and thus acquire the village of Roxheim into the bargain."

The count looked much abashed, but the noble guests only laughed heartily at the joke.

Thus stout Boos of Waldeck became lord of the village of Hüffelsheim.

*

THE FOUNDATION OF
CASTLE SPONHEIM

The following legend tells us about the origin of Castle Sponheim in the valley of the Nahe. Once a Knight of Ravensberg was eagerly wooing the beautiful young Countess of Heimburg, but there was a serious obstacle blocking his path to success. Some years before a Ravensberg had killed a Heimburg in a quarrel, and since that time a bitter feud had divided the two houses. The brave knight felt this bitterly, but in spite of it he did not leave off his wooing. The young countess was much touched by his constancy, and one day she spoke thus to her impetuous suitor:

"My lord, if you will dare to go to the Holy Land there to expiate the sins of your fathers, and bring me back a relic from the sepulchre of our Redeemer, in that same hour your suit will be heard."

The knight in great joy kissed the maiden's

slender hand and departed, carrying the memory of her sweet smile away in his heart.

Just at this time the call of the Emperor Barbarossa, now an old man, sounded throughout the land, and the Knight of Ravensberg did not neglect the opportunity, but hastened forth to join the imperial army.

The expedition was a long and terrible one, and the troops wearily made their way across the desert plains of Palestine.

The knight, though a brave man, had no special love for warlike adventures, and during these exhausting marches he thought sorrowfully of his quiet castle on the Nahe; of how he used to lie down there in peace and safety at night without being in fear of the Saracens who, under cover of darkness, would break in brandishing their scimitars, an event which was a nightly occurrence on this expedition.

Ravensberg however fought bravely in many a battle, and after the deaths of Barbarossa and his son, he joined the army of Richard the Lion-hearted.

Through all this anxious time he never forgot his dear one at home, and his longing for her became stronger every day, till it seemed to grow beyond endurance.

King Richard was called back to England on some urgent matters of state, and the Knight of Ravensberg was among the few companions-in-arms who embarked with him. The brave knight was very happy, and while the king's ship was sailing along the coast of Greece and up the blue Adriatic Sea, he would often stand on deck and weave bright dreams of the future; sometimes when no one was near, he would pull out a little black ebony box set with precious stones, on which a woman's name was written in golden letters; the interior was beautifully lined with costly silk, and a small splinter of wood lay within which the knight would kiss most reverently. He had paid a large sum of money for it in the Holy Land, where he had bought it from a Jewish merchant. This man had sworn to him that this fragment was from the cross to which the Son of God had been nailed.

The knight was very happy during this long homeward journey, but a great misfortune awaited him. Just as the crusaders came in sight of Italy their vessel was wrecked. The King of England, the Knight of Ravensberg, and a few others were saved with great difficulty, and brought to land. But our poor knight was inconsolable; he had held the precious little box high above him in the water, but a mighty wave had torn it from him, and on opening his eyes he found himself on shore. The holy relic had saved him, but he had lost his treasure, and now all hope of his promised happiness was gone.

———

One day a weary and dispirited crusader returned to the castle of Heimburg. He announced his arrival to the young countess most humbly, but she, her lovely face lighted by a bright smile, hurried to meet the knight whose sunburnt countenance betokened great hardships. She listened silently to his mournful story, then raising her beautiful head she asked: "Was not the little box set with precious stones, and was not my name in golden letters on it?"

"Yes, noble lady," said the knight, the bitterness of his disappointment sharply revived, "And now it lies at the bottom of the sea in spite of my fervent prayers to St. George to save the precious fragment of our Saviour's cross."

The countess beckoned to a page, and after a few minutes the boy brought her on a velvet cushion a little black ebony box set with precious stones with a woman's name written on it.

The knight uttered a cry of joyful surprise, for he recognised the jewel at once.

"Entreat the Holy Patron of Knighthood to pardon you," said the countess with a smile. "A strange knight brought this to the steward a few days ago, and before I had time to send for him, he had disappeared."

"It was St. George himself!" whispered the knight, crossing himself piously, "which proves that the fragment really belonged to the. Holy Cross."

Then he bent his knee before his charming mistress who, with a deep blush on her cheeks, gave the man she had long but secretly loved love's first kiss.

————

A happy marriage was speedily celebrated in Heimburg. The Knight of Ravensberg then named his castle Spanheim (Span being the German word for chip) in memory of the precious little relic. The name was later on corrupted into Sponheim.

ST. CLEMENT'S CHAPEL

There is a very melancholy legend connected with the foundation of St. Clement's church, which was built on the banks of the Rhine and which, not long since, was rebuilt and renovated by the generosity of the present great lady of Rheinstein Castle.

Rudolphus of Habsburg, elected emperor after the terrible anarchy which had reigned in Germany when the land was left without a ruler, determined by firm and vigorous government, to put an end to the evil-doings of the robber-knights who held sway along the Rhine.

He had already threatened these much-dreaded nobles who disturbed the peace of the country and the government of its ruler, and now hearing that they still continued their ravages, the emperor appeared in person in the Rhine countries, resolved to annihilate them and to destroy their strongholds.

On his way through the land, Rudolphus set fire to all the strongholds on the upper Rhine.

The burning of the castles of Reichenstein, Sooneck, Heimburg and others, was an awful sight to the inhabitants of the vally below. Numerous members of these ancient noble races met the death of felons, and their bodies were hung up on trees as a warning to others.

Through the gates of Mainz many a robber-baron was led as a prisoner by the soldiers of the emperor. Every time that one of these barons and his companions-in-arms were led along with bound hands, towards the imperial tribunal, young and old, rich and poor poured forth from the streets and alleys, and accompanied the high-born malefactors with curses. The windows of the houses around were filled with eager onlookers, admiring the conduct of their emperor.

Moaning and wailing were then heard throughout the land, mothers, wives, and daugthers, weeping for their dead. On the other hand the merchants who had endured hardship and sufferings during these years, were now delighted with the stern justice dealt out by the emperor.

Under cover of darkness stealthy forms could be seen creeping to the place of execution, and silently and mournfully taking away the bodies of their relatives to preserve them from ignominious destruction. They then buried the wretched remains in consecrated ground, hoping thus to satisfy the fears which haunted them of future punishment, for many of their dear ones had stained their swords with the blood of their neighbours

In order to atone for these sins, and in accordance with the wise counsel of a priest, the trees on which the bodies had been hanged were cut down, and the wood used to build a chapel of expiation. Stones were also taken from the smoking ruins of the burning castles and employed for the same purpose. The little church was built on the lonely place of execution on the Rhine near Assmannshausen.

The day arrived — a day of great sorrow and weeping — when all was ready, and the priest was to read prayers from the altar for the first time. Many funeral barges were to be seen on the river, bringing the dead.

The Archbishop of Mayence absolved the bodies from their sins, and afterwards they were all interred together near the little church for the second time.

This occurred towards the end of the thirteenth century. For long years afterwards prayers were offered up in this church in Assmannshausen for the soul's of the dead.

The once proud and mighty races gradually died out, and their strongholds fell into ruins. And time which had demolished the castles on the heights above, began her work of destruction on the little church below; its roof decayed and its walls crumbled.

The ancient little church of St. Clement has since that time been raised again from its ruins, and now the voice of God's priest is heard chanting in it again, as it was heard six hundred years ago.

*

Castle Rheinstein

THE WOOING

In Castle Rheinstein once lived a knight
called Diethelm, who devoted himself without
restraint to all the excesses of the robber barons.
From one of his pillaging expeditions he brought
back a charming maiden called Jutta. As the
delicate ivy twines itself round the rough oak
and clothes its knotty stem with shimmering
velvet, so in time the gentle conduct of this
maiden changed the coarse baron to a noble
knight who eschewed pillaging and carousing,
and ultimately made the fair Jutta the honoured
wife of her captor.

The first fruit of their love cost the tender
mother her life. Gerda however, who much
resembled her mother, grew to such a noble
beauty that soon wooers from far and near came
to sue for the hand of the beautiful daughter
of the aged Diethelm. But the aged knight
made a most careful selection, and many gay
wooers had to depart in sorrow. One young man
was however regarded favourably by the maid,

and not unkindly looked upon by the old man. He was the oldest son of the owner of the Sternburg. This young man had contrived to win the maiden's heart, and one day, while Gerda was presiding as queen of love and beauty at a tournament held in the courtyard of Castle Rheinstein, Helmbrecht made an avowal of his love.

Some days thereafter the young lord according to courtly fashion appointed his uncle Gunzelin of Reichenstein to woo his chosen bride for him. But Gunzelin though an old man was full of knavery and falsehood, and so instead of wooing for his nephew he ingratiated himself with Gerda's father. Moreover, as the old knight was descended from an ancient family and possessed of much wealth Diethelm was easily induced to promise him the hand of the fair Gerda. To the astonishment of this worthy pair Gerda would not listen to the suit of her rich wooer. Her heart belonged to the nephew, not the uncle. Now Count Diethelm was aroused, and with the blind fury of his earlier years swore to his rich companion that Gerda belonged to him, and should never wed the young cocksparrow of the Sternburg.

In her quiet chamber the unhappy maid wept out her heart's grief, but burning tears did not thaw the ice-cold heart of the father.

In vain the young lover tried to gain the old knight's favour, but Diethelm merely referred to his knightly word solemnly pledged to the lord of Reichenstein.

Soon the day approached on which Gunzelin with the smiling self satisfaction of an old roué, and decked out to give himself all the appearance of young manhood, was to lead the fairest maiden in the Rhineland to his stately castle. Gerda who possessed the mild disposition of her deceased mother had submitted to the inevitable. On a bright summer morning the bridal procession started from the courtyard of Castle Rheinstein, and moved towards the Clement's Chapel situated in the neighbourhood. Horns blew and trumpets sounded. On a milk-white palfrey, sat the fair young bride, deadly pale. She was thinking of her absent lover who at that moment must be enduring the greatest anguish on her account. Then all at once a swarm of buzzing gadflies came out of the bush and fastened fiercely on the palfrey which bore the fair Gerda. The animal reared and broke from the bridal procession. Boldly the bridegroom on his grandly caparisoned steed dashed forward to check the frightened animal, but his war-horse, missing its footing on the narrow bridle path, fell over a precipice carrying its master with it. The dying knight was carried by the wedding-guests back to Castle Rheinstein. The aged Diethelm was also unfortunate in his attempt to stop the runaway steed. The maddened animal had struck him on the shin-bone, and wounded him. The servants were thus obliged to carry the moaning greybeard back to his castle as speedily and carefully as possible. The surgeon had a sad time of it during the next week as he attended to the enraged old knight's wounds and bruises.

When the runaway horse had disappeared round a bend of the path a man threw himself upon it, and bringing the trembling animal to a standstill clasped the unconscious bride in his arms. Helmbrecht, concealed in the brushwood, had been watching the bridal procession, and now came to the rescue of his true love. When the old lord heard of this he came to his senses and gave the lovers his blessing. Some weeks later a bridal procession advanced from the Clement's Chapel up to the festively decorated Castle Rheinstein. Trumpets were blown and horns resounded. Much more joyfully than on the previous occasion the musicians marched in front. Upon a milk-white palfrey, as formerly, sat a noble maiden in bridal state, clothed in undulating robes bordered with fur. Her head was bent in maiden modesty as she listened to the endearments which the youthful knight whispered in her ear. Behind rode the father of the bride sunk in thought, and along with him was his pious sister Notburge, the canoness of Nonnenwerth.

A life of unalloyed married bliss followed this union, and God granted to the noble pair a long and happy life. They rest together in front of the altar in the Clement's Chapel which is situated across the Rhine from Assmannshausen. Burg Rheinstein has renewed its youth, and still from its precipitous height proudly overlooks the waters of our noble stream.

THE BLIND ARCHER

In his stronghold at Sooneck, Siebold, one of the most rapacious of the robber barons presided over a godless revel. Wanton women with showy apparel and painted cheeks lolled in the arms of tipsy cavaliers. The music blared, and to complete their carousal wine flowed freely. The lord of Sooneck flushed with drinking, and leering on the assembly with evil-looking eyes spoke as follows:

"Noble ladies (drunken applause from his worthy associates) and much-married nobles (the shameless females giggled loudly), after food and drink, I, as your host will be pleased to entertain you by bringing before you a ferocious animal which I keep confined here."

While the ladies pretended to take shelter timidly behind their lords, and the men stared at their host expecting some further explanation, the doors of the room opened, and led by two servants a man in coarse garments, and with unkempt hair and beard stood before them A suppressed whisper passed round the festive board and all eyes were fixed on the haggard countenance of the prisoner. When for a moment the weary eyelids were raised, two ghastly cavities were visible. Again, with the same tone of levity, the lord of the castle spoke, "Lovely ladies, and knightly companions, the best marksman on the Rhine was Hans Veit of Fürsteneck. Like ourselves he was dreaded far and near. He and I entered on a feud of life and death. He went down."

"With broken blade and battered shield, bleeding from numerous wounds I lay prostrate before you awaiting manfully the death-thrust," murmured the prisoner, and his voice sounded as if from the grave. "It pained me to finish him off," said Siebold flippantly, "I got his two eyes taken out, and thus added to my collection of rarities, the best archer on the Rhine."

"My murdered eyes behold your scorn," said the prisoner harshly. "But surely chivalry still flourishes on Sooneck" said the lord of the castle. "Understand then that my servants have informed me, that even blind, you can, guided only by sounds, hit a given mark with a bolt. If you come out of this ordeal successful, freedom shall be the reward". Stormy applause greeted these words.

"Death were dearer to me than life," murmured the blind archer. As he seized the crossbow however, a gleam of joy went over his countenance like a ray of sunshine over a sombre landscape. Crowded together in a corner of the room the guests watched the proceedings. The lord of Sooneck seized a goblet and ordered the prisoner to draw upon it, after hearing the sound. In the next moment the silver clang resounded, as the goblet fell on the floor.

"Shoot now," said Siebold of Sonneck, and immediately an arrow pierced his mouth. With a grunt like a slaughtered ox, Siebold sank among the rushes. Silent and motionless with the two eye-cavities gaping, stood the blind man. Then his shaggy head sank on his heaving breast. Like a flock of frightened crows the knights and their paramours fled, and only a few terrified squires and servants muttered prayers over the body of the lord of Sooneck.

*

The Ruins of Fürstenberg

THE MOTHER'S GHOST

Lambert of Fürstenberg was a hearty jovial knight, and had married Wiltrud, a daughter of the Florsheim family. He was attached to his gentle wife, who had just presented him with a son and heir. But an evil genius entered the castle in the person of a noble maiden called Luckharde. This maiden who had suddenly been left an orphan, belonged to a family long befriended by the house of Fürstenberg. She was only eighteen, but possessed a lascivious beauty, very dangerous to men.

The lady of the castle, who had been in delicate health since the birth of her child, gave Luckharde a warm-hearted welcome into the bosom of her family, trusting that the young woman would be of great service to her in the management of her little realm, and would repay her kindness by sisterly love and sympathy, Luckharde however was of a vain and frivolous disposition, and had little love for household affairs, or womanly duties.

As the months passed, Luckharde's ripening and dangerous beauty gained gradually and almost imperceptibly more and more influence over the susceptible heart of the lord of the castle, and soon the day came when he yielded himself entirely to the charms of this beautiful woman. Wildtrud's eyes were by no means blind to the shameful ingratitude of the adulteress, and the godless conduct of her husband. Her weakness however, prevented her from calling down the judgment of heaven on the sinners. Luckharde, led on by her unbridled passion, now formed a devilish design which would enable her to take the place of the lawful wife of Lambert. One night she slipped into the chamber of the lady of the castle, approached the bed of the sleeping woman with a cat-like step, and smothered her with the pillows, the poor invalid offering but a feeble and ineffective resistance.

Wiltrud's death was deeply mourned by the household, who believed that she had died of a broken heart. Lambert too might be grieved, but in the arms of his raven-locked enchantress he soon forgot his deceased wife, and in a few weeks Luckharde was made lady of Fürstenberg. The little boy whom Wiltrud had borne to her unfaithful husband was hateful to the second wise, who fondled her lord, and flattered him with the hope of the children she would bear him. Then it was arranged that the knight's first-born should be handed over to the care of an old crone who lived in a remote tower of the castle.

One night this old woman awoke suddenly, and was terrified to see a female form dressed in a flowing white robe, bending over the cradle of the little boy, who slept near. The woman seemed to be tending the child, and after blessing him, she vanished. The old woman crossed herself, and in terror muttered many prayers. In the early morning she hurried to her new mistress in great agitation and with white lips told her of her strange visitor. Luckharde at first laughed in her usual frivolous manner at this ridiculous ghost story, but soon she became more serious and alarmed. Then she ordered the old woman to arrange her bed beside the other servants, but still to leave the child in the tower-chamber. A dreadful fear had taken possession of Luck-harde's guilty soul. Perhaps people were deceived when they believed Wiltrud to be dead, and it was thus that she returned at night to nurse her child.

Then this daring and sinful woman prepared a bed for herself in the lonely tower beside the child. She also brought with her a formidable dagger, and thus she awaited what the night might bring forth. At midnight the female figure dressed in the flowing white robe appeared once more. It approached the cradle of the child, tended him and blessed him. Then the terror-stricken Luckharde stared motionless at the apparition as it rose and approached her bed. Towering there above her were the pallid features of the dead Wiltrud, and the lifeless entreating eyes looked steadily at this sinful woman who had taken the place of her benefactress. To Luckharde it seemed as if a towering cliff was slowly bending over to overwhelm her. With a last mad effort the wretched woman seized the dagger; and struck at the apparition; but she might as well have struck at a misty cloud. Now Luckharde perceived that she was in the presence of the murdered lady of the Fürstenberg, and harrowed with the thought of her guilt she seemed to hear a voice as if from another world saying, "Do penance for thy sins."

Next morning Lambert waited in vain for his wife to appear. On looking around however he noticed a piece of parchment. On it Luckharde had confessed with deep sorrow, how she had murdered his first wife in order to further her evil designs, and how the spirit of the dead had appeared to her in the night, and reminded her of her great guilt. She was going to fly to a cloister to do penance during the remainder of her days, and she recommended her sinful accomplice to do the same. Lambert of Fürstenberg was deeply grieved on hearing this revelation. He handed over his castle and child to a younger brother, and spent the rest of this life as a solitary hermit.

*

BURG STAHLECK

Ancient Bacharach was once a famous place, and long before the fiery wine that grows there became famous throughout the world — "it was in the good old times as our grandmothers say" — it was the delight of many a connoisseur abroad. About that time its grateful lovers erected an altar to Bacchus who provided them so liberally with wine. The place of sacrifice was on a huge rock projecting out of the Rhine, between an island and the right bank of the river, and in honour of the god they gave the town the name it still bears.

The inscriptions on the altar-stone have become unintelligible, but the Bacharach folk know well to the present day the original meaning of them.

Fishermen still keep up the old custom but now more as an amusement; they dress up a straw-man as Bacchus, place him on the altar, and surround him singing.

The ruins of the castle of Stahleck are situated

on the Rhine, above the wild, romantic country of Bacharach.

About the time of Conrad III. the first Emperor of the House of Hohenstaufen, a ambitious young knight, Palatinate Count Hermann, inhabited this castle. Being a nephew of the emperor, this aspiring knight considered his high and mighty relationship as a sufficient reason for enlarging his dominions.

He conceived no less a plan than that of taking possession of part of the property which bordered on his land, belonging to the Archbishops of Mayence and Treves, supporting his claim by declaring that for more than one reason he had a right of possession. The jealousy which at that time existed between the clerical and the secular powers, brought a number of neighbouring knights to his side as allies, and the count began his unprovoked quarrel by taking a castle at Treves on the Moselle by storm. This castle belonged to the diocese of that town.

Adalbert of Monstereil, a man of an undaunted character, was then Bishop both of Treves and Metz.

He at once collected his warriors to drive the bold robber from the conquered castle. The temerity of the count and his superior forces dismayed Adalbert, giving him grounds for sober reflections. But the good bishop was a clever man and, not believing himself sufficiently strong to resist the count, he sought refuge in spiritual weapons.

When his people were about to assault the stronghold, he made a most enthusiastic speech to his troops.

Holding up a crucifix in his right hand, he told to them that in the silent hours of the previous night the Archangel Michael had appeared to him, and had given him this crucifix, at the same time promising him certain victory if each of his warriors attacked the enemy in the firm belief that an invincible Higher Power was near to help them.

The bishop's words inspired his men with a great courage. Led on by the holy man carrying the crucifix in his raised hand, they marched on to the assault, stormed the castle, and made Hermann's troops flee in great confusion. The ambitious count, now finding himself deserted by his troops, was forced to renounce the feud which he had hoped to carry on against the bishop.

———

The disgraceful defeat the count had suffered was most humiliating to him, but it had not killed his ambition.

He now directed his thoughts to his other ecclesiastical neighbour.

Having searched through some ancient documents, he thought he had found full right to a strip of land which Arnold of Solnhofen, Bishop of Mayence, then held in his possession. He at once sent in his claim to this mighty prince of the church, who received it with a scornful laugh. "Oh!" said the bishop, tearing up the written complaint, "I shall be able to manage this little count as well as I have all along managed the stubborn people of Mayence, some of whom have bitterly repented of having rebelled against their bishop."

Hermann was told how Solnhofen had treated his claim. In great wrath he swore to take vengeance on the man who had dared to tear up his complaint so insolently. His young wife implored him with tears in her eyes not to raise his hand against a servant of the Lord again. But he turned contemptuously away.

Hermann was well aware that, through the influence of the bishop's companions-in-arms, he was now hated by the citizens of Mayence. This circumstance made him determine to rob

Arnold of land and dignity, as he ascribed the cause of this deadly dissension to the power the bishop exerted over the people of his diocese.

The count, now joined by several daring knights, again prepared to make war against the representative of the church, and marched to attack the bishop in his stronghold.

Arnold was enraged at this persistent striving against the dominions of the church, and his dark soul conceived a dastardly plan to rid them of their enemy. He hired two villains who treacherously put he count to death.

Soon afterwards the rebellious citizens of Mayence successfully stormed the bishop's palace and turned the cruel prelate out of his episcopal seat, whereupon he was obliged to flee for his life. But Arnold was not so easily subdued and he soon returned, breathing vengeance. His friends warned him in vain, and even the famous prophetess, Hildegarde of Rupertusberg, sent a messenger to him with the words, "Turn to the Lord whom you have forsaken, your hour is near at hand."

But he heeded not this admonition, and at last he was killed by the rebels in the Abbey of Jacobsberg, some distance from the town where he had taken up his residence.

Kaub

CASTLE GUTENFELS

About the middle of the thirteenth century, there was a stately castle near Kaub which was inhabited by Count Philip of Falkenstein. There he lived very happily with his beautiful sister Guta, who was as good as she was fair.

Numerous knights had sought to win her love, but none had achieved this conquest, the castle maiden having no desire to exchange her brother's hospitable home for any other.

At that time a magnificent tournament was held at Cologne, to which knights from all countries of the kingdom far and near and even from England were invited.

A great multitude of spectators were assembled to see the stately knights contending for the prize, which a fair hand would bestow on them.

Among the nobles present at the tournament was a knight from England, whose graceful figure and splendid armour were particularly striking. He wore a veiled visor, and the stewards of the tournament announced him under the name of "the Lion Knight," a golden lion ornamenting his shield. Soon the majestic knight's masterly manner of fighting created a great sensation, and when he succeeded in unhorsing his opponent, a most formidable combatant, loud rejoicings rang through the lists.

Count Philip and his sister were among the guests. Guta had been watching the strange knight with ever increasing interest during the tournament, regretting at the same time that she could not see his face.

But an opportunity soon presented itself when the knight was declared victor. When she was selected to present the prize, a golden laurel-wreath, to the winner, she became much embarrassed, and a feeling such as she had never before experienced seized her as she looked at the Briton's face for the first time.

Perhaps the knight may have read in the lovely maiden's countenance what she in vain tried to hide from him, perhaps a spark from that passionate fire which had so suddenly fired her heart, may have flown into his soul as he knelt before her to receive the wreath, which she placed on his head with a trembling hand. Who can tell?

Afterwards when these two were conversing together in subdued whispers, the knight silently admiring her grace and the maiden scarcely able to restrain her feelings, the thoughts which he longed to tell her, flamed in his heart. The same evening in the banqueting hall, when the music was sounding within its walls, he was Guta's inseparable companion, and eloquent words flowed from his lips telling her of the love which his eyes betrayed.

The proud stranger begged Guta for her love and swore to be hers; he told her he must at once return to his country where urgent duty called him, but that he would come back to claim her in three months' time. Then he would publicly sue for her hand and declare his name, which circumstances compelled him to keep secret for the time being.

Love will make any sacrifice; Guta accepted her lover's pledge willingly, and thus they parted under the assurance that they would soon meet again.

Five months had passed. That terrible time ensued when Germany became the battlefield of the party-struggles over the election of the emperor. Conrad IV. the last of the house of Hohenstaufen, had died in Italy. In the northern countries there was a great rising against William of Holland who was struggling for the imperial throne; Alphonso of Castile was chosen king in one part of the country, while Richard of Cornwall, son of John, king of England, was elected in another; but Richard, having received most influential votes, was crowned at Aix-la-Chapelle, and from thence he started on a journey through the Rhine provinces, to the favour of which he had been chiefly indebted for his election.

———

Spring was casting her bright beams over waves and mountains in the valley of the Rhine, but in Falkenstein castle no ray of sunshine penetrated the gloom. Guta, pale and unhappy, sat within its walls, weaving dreams which seemed destined never to be fulfilled. Sometimes she saw her lover dying on a terrible battle field with her name on his lips, then again laughing and bright with a maiden from that far-off island in his arms, talking derisively of his sweetheart on the Rhine. She became more and more conscious that she had given him her first love, and that he had cruelly deceived er. Sorrow and grief had taken possession of her, and all her brother's efforts to amuse her and to distract her attention were in vain.

A great sound of trumpets was heard one day on the highway, and a troop of knights stopped at the castle. Guta saw the train of warriors from her window, where she had been sitting weeping. The count with chivalrous hospitality received them, and led them into the banqueting-hall. His astonishment was great, when he recognised the bold Briton, the victor at the tournament in Cologne, as leader of this brilliant retinue, he who had broken his secret pledge to his beloved sister. A dark glance took the place of the friendly expression on his face. The Briton seemed to notice it and pressing Philip's hand said cordially, "I am Richard of Cornwall, elected Emperor of Germany, and I have come here to solicit the hand of your sister Guta, who promised herself to me five months ago in Cologne. I come late to redeem my promise, but my love is unchanged. I beg you to announce my arrival to her without betraying my name."

Philip bowed deeply before the illustrious guest, and the retainers respectfully retired to a distance. The great guest strode up and down the room impatiently. Then the doors were suddenly thrown open, and a beautiful figure appeared on the threshold, her face glowing with emotion.

With a low cry Guta threw herself into her lover's arms, and the first moments of their reunion were passed in silent happiness.

Philip now entered the room unperceived, and revealed the secret to his sister. The maiden in great confusion and shame stole a look at her lover's eyes, and he, drawing her gently to him, asked her to share all — even his throne with him.

Shortly afterwards Richard celebrated his marriage with imperial magnificence at the castle on the Rhine, which Philip thence forward called Gutenfels, in honour of his sister.

Oberwesel

THE SEVEN MAIDENS

The scattered ruins of an old knight's tower are still to be seen on one of the heights near Oberwesel. The castle was called Schönberg, after the seven virgins who once lived there, and whose beauty was renowned throughout all the Rhine countries.

Their father had died early, some say of grief, because Heaven had denied him a son, and an elderly aunt had striven in vain to guide the seven wild sisters; but her influence had not been sufficiently strong to lead them in the right way. After the death of this relative the seven beautiful maidens were left to themselves, and now their longing after liberty and the pleasures of the world broke out even stronger than before.

Many a tale was told about them, how they used to ride out hunting and hawking, how many a magnificent banquet was given by them, and how their beauty, their riches, and the gay and joyous life led by them attracted many knights from near and far; how many a stately noble came to their castle to woo one of the sisters, and how these maidens at first ensnared and enchanted him with a thousand attractive charms, only in the end to reject the enamoured suitor with scorn and mockery.

Ashamed and very wrathful many a great knight had left the castle, and with indignation and disdain had blotted out of his memory the names of these bewitching sirens who at first had listened with deceitful modesty to his honest wooing, only afterwards to declare with scornful laughter that their liberty was so dear to them, that they would not give it up for the sake of any man.

Alas! there were always youths to be found who put no faith in such speeches and, trusting to their great namens and peculiar merits, sought their happiness among these maidens. But all the trials ended in the same mournful manner; no suitor succeeded in winning the heart of these seductive beings. Thus they continued their dangerous and contemptible life for some years.

Once again there was a great banquet and feasting in the halls of the castle. A circle of knightly figures sat round the brilliant board among the seven sisters, who were quite conscious of their charms, one rivalling the other in gaiety and liveliness.

The joyous scene was disturbed for a short time by two knights who were disputing about one of the sisters, and had angered each other by their growing jealousy.

The scene excited general attention and was looked on at first as a most amusing one, but when the youths were about to draw their swords, it was thought necessary to separate them.

Seizing this opportunity one of the other knights proposed, that to guard against further discord, the castle maidens should be urged to make a final decision, so that each suitor — they all recognised one another as such — might know what he had to expect.

The proposal met with general applause, only the sisters showed discontentment, declaring they could not agree to such a presumptuous plan. However the wooers tried every imaginable means of persuading them, and at last one of the sisters wavered, a second followed her example, and the remaining ones after whispering to each other for some time, declared with laughing countenances that they would decide the fate of their suitors the next day.

The expected hour arrived, and the knights in great suspense assembled in the large hall.

Every eye was riveted on the door through which these Graces should enter, bringing a sweet surprise to some or a bitter disappointment to others.

The folding doors were suddenly thrown open, and an attendant announced that the mistresses of the castle were waiting to receive the knights in the garden near the river.

The numerous suitors all hurried out. To their great astonishment they saw the fair ones all seated in a boat on the Rhine. With a peculiar smile they beckoned the knights to approach, and the eldest sister, standing up in her seat, made the following speech.

"You may all throw your hopes to the winds, for not one of us would dream of falling in love with you, much less of marrying you. Our liberty is much too precious to us, and we shall not sacrifice it for any man. We are going to sail down to Cologne to the property of a relative, and there we shall disappoint other suitors, just as we have misled you, my noble lords. Good-bye, good-bye!"

The scornful speech was accompanied by a scoffing laugh which was re-echoed by the other sisters, and the boat set sail.

The rejected suitors stood speechless with shame and anger.

Suddenly a terrible storm arose, the boat was agitated violently, and the laughter of the seven sisters was turned to cries for help. But the roaring of the waves drowned their voices, and the billows rushed over the boat, burying it and the seven sisters in the depths below.

Just on the spot where these stony-hearted maidens met their deaths, seven pointed rocks appeared above the surface of the water, which up to the present day are still to be seen, a salutary warning to all the young maidens of the country.

*

LORELEI

Above Coblentz where the Rhine flows through hills covered with vineyards, there is a steep rock, round which many a legend has been woven — the Lurlei Rock. The boatman gazes up at its gigantic summit with awe-struck reverence when his boat glides over the waters at twilight. Like chattering children the restless waves whisper round the rock, telling wonderful tales of its doings. Above on its gray head, the legend relates that a beautiful but false nymph, clothed in white with a wreath of stars in her flowing hair, used to sit and sing sweet songs, until a sad tragedy drove her forever away.

Long long ago, when night in her dark garment descended from the hills, and her silent comrade, the pale moon, cast a silver bridge over the deep green stream, the soft voice of a woman was heard from the rock, and a creature of divine beauty was seen on its summit. Her golden locks flowed like a queenly mantle from her graceful shoulders, covering her snow-white raiment so that her tenderly-formed body appeared like a cloud of light. Woe to the boatsman who passed the rock at the close of day! As of old, men were fascinated by the heavenly song of the Grecian hero, so was the unhappy voyager lured by this being into sweet forgetfulness, his eyes, even as his soul, would be dazzled, and he could no longer steer clear of reefs and cliffs, and this beautiful siren only drew him to an early grave. Forgetting all else, he would steer towards her, already dreaming of having reached her; but the jealous waves would wash round his boat and at last dash him treacherously against the rocks. The roaring waters of the Rhine would drown the cries of agony of the victim who would never be seen again.

But the virgin to whom no one had ever approached, continued every night to sing soft and low, till darkness vanished in the first rays of light, and the great day-star drove the gray mists from the valley.

II.

Ronald was a proud youth and the boldest warrior at the court of his father, the Palatinate

Count. He heard of this divine, enchanting creature, and his heart burned with the desire to behold her. Before having seen the waternymph, he felt drawn to her by an irresistible power.

Under pretence of hunting, he left the court, and succeeded in getting an old sailor to row him to the rock. Twilight was brooding over the valley of the Rhine when the boat approached the gigantic cliff; the departing sun had long sunk below the mountains, and now night was creeping on in silence; the evening star was twinkling in the deep blue firmament. Was it his guardian-angel who had placed it there as a warning to the deluded young man?

He gazed at it in rapture for some time, until a low cry from the old man at his side interrupted him. "The Lorelei!" whispered he, startled, "do you see her — the enchantress?" The only answer was a soft murmur which escaped from the youth. With wide-open eyes he looked up and lo! there she was. Yes, this was she, this wonderful creature! A glorious picture in a dark frame. Yes, that was her golden hair, and those were her flowing white garments.

She was hovering up above on the rocks combing her beautiful hair; rays of light surrounded her graceful head, revealing her charms in spite of the night and the distance, und as he gazed, her lips opened, and a song thrilled through the silence, soft and plaintive like the sweet notes of a nightingale on a still summer evening.

From her height she looked down into the hazy distance and cast at the youth a rapturous look which sank down into his soul, thrilling his whole frame.

His eyes were fixed on the features of this celestial being where he read the sweet story of love . . . Rocks, stream, glorious night, all melted into a mist before his eyes, he saw nothing but the figure above, nothing but her radiant eyes. The boat crept along, too slowly for him, he could no longer remain in it, and if his ear did not deceive him, this creature seemed to whisper his name with unutterable sweetness, and calling to her, he dashed into the water.

A death-like cry echoed from the rocks . . . and the waves sighed and washed over the unhappy youth's corpse.

The old boatman moaned and crossed himself, and as he did so, lightning tore the clouds asunder, and a loud peal of thunder was heard over the mountains. Then the waves whispered gently below, and again from the heights above, sad and dying away, sounded the Lurlei's song.

———

III.

The sad news was soon brought to the Palatinate Count, who was overpowered with grief and anger. He ordered the false enchantress to be delivered up to him, dead or alive.

The next day a boat sailed down the Rhine, manned by four hardy bold warriors. The leader looked up sternly at the great rocks which seemed to be smiling silently down at him. He had asked permission to dash the diabolical seducer from the top of the rocks into the foaming whirlpool below, where she would find a certain death, and the count had readily agreed to this plan of revenge.

———

IV.

The first shades of twilight were gliding softly over mountain and hill.

The rock was surrounded by armed men, and the leader, followed by some daring comrades, was climbing up the side of the mountain the top of which was veiled in a golden mist, which the men thought were the last rays of sunset. It was a bright gleam of light enshrouding the nymph who appeared on the rocks, dreamingly combing her golden hair. She then took a string of pearls from her bosom, and with her slender white hand bound them round her forehead. She cast a mocking glance at the threatening men approaching her.

"What are the weak sons of the earth seeking up here on the heights?" said she, moving her rosy lips scornfully. "You sorceress!" cried the leader enraged, adding with a contemptuous smile, "You! We shall dash you down into the river below!"

An echoing laugh was heard over the mountain.

"Oh! the Rhine will come himself to fetch me!" cried the maiden.

Then bending her slender body over the precipice yawning below, she tore the jewels from her forehead, hurling them triumphantly into the waters, while in a low sweet voice she sang: —

> "Haste thee, haste thee oh father dear!
> Send forth thy steeds from the waters clear.
> I will ride with waves and the wind!"

Then a storm burst forth, the Rhine rose, covering its banks with foam. Two gigantic billows like snow-white steeds rose out of the depths, and carried the nymph down into the rushing current.

————

V.

The terrified messengers returned to the count, bringing him the tidings of this wonderful event.

Ronald, whose body a chance wave had washed up on the banks of the river, was deeply mourned throughout the country.

From this time forth, the Lorelei was never seen again. Only when night sheds her dark shadow on the hills, and the pale moon weaves a silver bridge over the deep green stream, then the voice of a woman, soft and low, is heard echoing from the weird heights of the rocks.

— — —

The Lorelei has vanished, but her charm still remains.

Thou canst find it, O Wanderer, in the eyes of the maidens near the Rhine. It blooms on their cheeks, it lingers on their rosy lips, there thou wilt find its traces.

Arm thy heart, steel thy will, blindfold thine eye!

As a poet of the Rhine once wisely and warningly sang, "My son, my son, beware of the Rhine . . ."

The Lorelei has vanished, but her charm still remains.

ST. GEORGE'S LINDEN

The ruins of Castle Rheinfels, which stand above the pretty little town of St. Goar, are the most extensive of their kind on the Rhine. The castle was erected in the middle of the 13th century by Count Dietherr, a nobleman belonging to the famous Rhenish family of Katzenelnbogen. It was a strongly fortified burg, and within ten years of its completion the mighty ramparts witnessed several bloody encounters. Twenty-six Rhenish cities once combined to storm the invulnerable fortress, but though some 4000 lives were sacrificed the army retreated baffled. For centuries after this, the banner of the Hessian Landgraf waved from its battlements, none daring to attack it. Then the fanatic Gallic forces of the Revolution entered the Rhineland, and laid the magnificent castle in ruins.

There is a legend associated with Rheinfels which dates from that age of chivalry when noble knights and their squires trod its courts, and this legend seems touched with the sadness of the history of the castle itself. The Count of Rheinfels was the proud father of a lovely daughter, and among her numerous wooers it was George Brömser of Rüdesheim who had won the maiden's heart. No one was more incensed at this than the knight of Berg. This knight belonged indeed to a race said to have been descended from an archbishop of Cologne, but his disposition was evil, and his covetousness and avarice made him wish to increase what earthly possessions he had. But the lord of Rheinfels was shrewd enough and hesitated before entrusting his pretty daughter and her large dowry to such a man. As already remarked this entirely agreed with the maiden's desire. She was really deeply in love with the chivalrous young knight of Rüdesheim, but shrank, almost with aversion, from the impetuous wooing of the harsh and selfish knight of Berg.

Some time after the betrothal of the lovers the date of the marriage was fixed. Before the marriage had been celebrated however young Brömser appeared at Rüdesheim in the early dawn on his steaming war-horse, having ridden during the night from Rüdesheim to bring the following sad intelligence to his beloved. The Emperor Albrecht had summoned the nobles to do battle against the Swiss confederates, who had renounced their allegiance, driven the imperial representatives from their land, and finally declared war against their overlord. The knights of the Rhineland were called upon to suppress the flames of rebellion. On receiving the pressing call of the Emperor, Brömser did not hesitate for a moment but resolved to obey his feudal superior.

At first the young bride wept, but when her lover comforted her with words of endearment, and her father praised the soldierly resolution of the young man, the maiden calmly submitted to the will of God. Before the young knight rode off he took a young linden-tree which he had pulled up in a grove, and having removed the soil with his sword, he planted the sapling in front of the castle. Then he spoke as follows to his bride. "Tend this budding linden which I have planted here to the honour of my patron saint. You shall keep troth with me so long as it flourishes, but if it fade (and may St. George in his grace prevent it) then you may forget me, for I shall be dead." The weeping bride threw herself in her lover's arms, and while he enfolded her gently with his right, with his left he raised his sword, and showed her engraved upon it in ancient letters, for daily repetition, the words: "Preserve O everlasting God, the body here, the soul hereafter. Help, knight St. George." Then, after receiving many kind wishes from his sorrowing friends, the young soldier rode in the morning mist down through the woods to join the imperial forces.

Several months passed. Then the melancholy news got abroad in the German land that something disastrous had happened in the campaign against the Swiss peasants. At last came a trustworthy report to the effect that a bloody defeat had overtaken the proud army of Albrecht. It was at Morgarten, where the noble hero called Arnold of Winkelried had opened up to his countrymen a pathway to freedom over his spear-pierced body. Many counts and barons found on that day a grave in the land of the Swiss, and sounds of mourning were to be heard in many a German castle. But to Castle Rheinfels no traveller brought any tidings either of weal or woe, and we can imagine with what sickness of heart the maiden waited, and how her hope faded as the days and weeks slipped past. It was so long since the ill-fated army had set out against the Forest Cantons, and now the thoughts of men were turned in other directions, while the Swiss peasants were quietly allowed to reap the fruits of their bravery. The most sanguine found it difficult to cheer the drooping maiden of Castle Rheinfels.

Then one day her former wooer, the mean avaricious Dietrich of Berg, presented himself. It was certain that George Brömser must be dead, and he was come again to sue for the hand of so desirable a young lady. The dejected maiden informed her eager wooer that she had plighted her troth to her absent lover beside the linden-tree flourishing in front of the castle. Only when this tree, consecrated to St. George, should fade would she be released from her promise. The knight of Berg departed in anger, and immediately betook himself to a wood and there selected a decayed linden, as similar as possible to the green one growing before Castle Rheinfels. In the night he cautiously approached the castle, tore up the linden, flung it with a curse into the Rhine, and then planted in its place the withered sapling. Next morning, a morning bright with the promise of spring, the fair daughter of Rheinfels stepped out on the lawn. A cry of pain escaped her lips when she perceived the faded tree. The days and weeks that followed were spent in deep grief. After a suitable time had elapsed, the knight of Berg again put in an appearance at Rheinfels, mightily pleased with himself. Again

117

he sought the hand of the maiden now released from her solemn promise. Sadly, but firmly
however she told her importunate wooer that
she would keep troth with her lover in death
as in life. Then the wrath of the despised knight
drove him to commit a horrible deed. In his
savage anger he drew his sword and buried it
in the maiden's breast. Fleeing from the scene
of his dreadful crime he was suddenly seized with
remorse, and like Our Lord's avaricious disciple,
he went and hanged himself. Deep was the
sorrow in Castle Rheinfels over the sacrifice
of this innocent young bride, who had kept her
troth so nobly. But grief and tears could not
replace the lost one. In the midst of the mourning a stranger was announced. He came from
the Swiss land.

After the battle of Morgarten a brave Swiss
had found George Brömser with broken limbs
and many bleeding wounds amongst a heap of
slain. In a peasant's hut the wounded man lay
long in pain and weakness. His broken limbs
required long and patient attention. Finally, after
much suffering, George Brömser, the last of all
the campaigners rode back to the Rhineland,
with his lover's name on his lips and her image
in his heart.

With uncovered head the lord of Rheinfels

showed the young man the grave of his beloved, and there the two men embraced each other long and silently. The young soldier pulled up the faded linden-tree and hurled it into the Rhine, while on the newly-made grave he planted white lilies. George Brömser did not a second time fall in love, but remained true to his chosen bride to the end of his days. We are told that in the company of knightly minstrels he sought to forget his great sorrow, and that later he composed many pretty songs. One of them has survived the centuries, and was recently discovered, along with the melody in an old manuscript. It begins:

"A linden stands in yonder vale,
Ah God! what does it there?"

Sterrenberg and Liebenstein

THE BROTHERS

I.

In the middle ages, an old knight belonging to the court of the Emperor Conrad II. lived in a castle called Sternberg, near Boppard. The old warrior had two sons left to him. His wife had died many years before, and since her death, merry laughter had seldom been heard in the halls of the beautiful castle.

Soon a ray of sunshine seemed to break into these solemn rooms; a distant cousin at Rüdesheim had died, leaving his only child, a beautiful young girl, to the care of his relative.

The golden-haired Angela became the pet of the castle, and won the affection and friendship of the two sons by her engaging ways. What had already happened hundred of times now happened among these young people, love replaced the friendship of the two young knights, and both tried to win the maiden's favour.

The old master of the castle noticed this change, and his father's heart forebode trouble.

Both sons were equally dear to him, but perhaps his first born, who had inherited his mother's gentle character, fulfilled his heart's desire more than the fiery spirit of Conrad the younger.

From the first moment when the orphan appeared at his family seat, he had conceived the thought that his favourite son Henry, who was heir to his name and estates, would marry the maiden.

Henry loved Angela with a profound, sincere feeling which he seldom expressed.

His brother, on the contrary, made no secret of his ardent love, and soon the old man perceived with sorrow that the beautiful girl returned his younger son's passionate love. Henry, too, was not unaware of the happiness of this pair, and in generous self-denial he tried to bury his grief, and to rejoice heartily in his brother's success.

The distress of the elder brother did not escape Angela. She was much moved when she first remarked that his voice trembled on pronouncing her name, but soon love dazzled her eyes, so that the cloulds on his troubled countenance passed unnoticed by her.

About this time St. Bernhard of Clairvaux came from France to the Rhine, preaching a second crusade against the Infidels. The fiery words of the saintly monk roused many thousands to action; his appeal likewise reached the castle of Sternberg.

Henry, though not envying his brother's happiness, felt that it would be impossible for him to be a constant witness of it, and thus he was glad to answer this call, and to take up the cross.

Conrad, too longing for action and dominated by the impulse of the moment, was stirred up by the witching charms which a crusade to Palestine offered. His adventurous soul, cramped up in this castle so far removed from the world, thirsted for the adventures, which he imagined were awaiting the crusaders in the far off East. In vain the tears and prayers of the young girl were shed, in vain was the sorrow of his father who begged him not to desert him.

The old man was in despair about the unbending resolutions of his sons.

"Who will remain at the castle of my forefathers, if you both abandon it now, perhaps never to return," cried he sorrowfully. "I implore you, my eldest son, you, the very image of your mother, to have pity on your father's gray hairs. And you, Conrad, have pity on the tears of your betrothed." The brothers remained silent. Then the eldest grasped the old man's hand, saying gently.

"I shall not leave you, my father."

"And you, Angela," said the younger to the weeping maiden, "you will try and bear this separation, and will plant a sprig of laurel to make a wreath for me when I return."

———

II.

The next day the young knight left the home of his forefathers. At first the maiden seemed inconsolable in her grief. But soon her love began to slumber like a tired child; on awakening from this drowsiness indignation seized her, whispering complainingly in her ear, and disturbing all the sweet memories in which the picture of her light-hearted lover gleamed forth, he who had parted from her for the sake of empty glory.

Now left to herself, she began to consider the proud youth who was forced to live under

123

the same roof with his rejected love. She admired his good qualities which all seeemed to have escaped her before, has great daring at the chase, his skill with weapons, and his many kind acts of pure friendship to her, with the view of sweetening the bitter separation from which she was suffering.

He seemed afraid of rousing the love which was still sleeping in his heart.

In the meantime Angela felt herself drawn more and more towards the knight; she wished to try and make him understand that her love for his younger brother had only been a youthful passion, which seemed to have flown when he left her. She felt unhappy when she understood that Henry, whom she now began really to love, seemed to feel nothing but brotherly affection for her, and she longed in her inmost soul for a word of love from him.

Henry was not unaware of this change in her affections, but he proudly smothered every rising thought in his heart for his brother's betrothed.

The old knight was greatly pleased when, one day, Angela came to him, and with tears in her eyes disclosed to him the secret of her heart.

124

He prayed God fervently to bring these two loving hearts together whom he believed were destined for one another by the will of God. In his dreams he already saw Angela in her castle like his dead wife and his first-born son, rocking her little baby, a blue-eyed, fair-haired child. Then he would suddenly recollet his impetuous younger son fighting in the crusades, and his dreams would be hastily interrupted.

Just opposite his ancestral hall he caused a proud fort to be built, and called it "Liebenstein," intending it for his second son when he returned from the Holy Land. The castle was hardly finished, when the old man died.

The crusade at last was at an end. All the knights from the Rhine country brought back the news with them on their return from the Holy Land, that Conrad had married a beautiful Grecian woman in the East, and was now on his way home with her.

Henry was beside himself with wrath on hearing this news. Such dishonourable conduct and shameful neglect seemed impossible to him, and going to the maiden he informed her of his brother's approaching return.

She turned very pale, her lips moved, but her tongue found no words.

———

III.

A large ship was seen one day sailing along the Rhine with strange flags waving on its masts. Angela saw it from her tower where she now spent many a long day reflecting on her unfortunate destiny, and she hastily called up the elder brother.

The ship approached nearer and nearer. Soon the cries of the boatmen could be heard, and the faces of the crew could be distinguished.

Suddenly the maiden uttered a cry, and threw herself weeping into the arms of the knight. The latter gazed at the vessel, his brows contracted. Yes! there on board, in shining armour, stood his brother, with a beautiful strange woman clinging to his arm.

The ship touched land. One of the first, Conrad sprang on shore. The two watchers in the tower disappeared. A man approached Conrad and informed him that the new castle was destined for him. The same day the impetuous knight sent notice of his arrival to Sternberg castle, but his brother answered him, that he would wait for him on the bridge, but would only meet sword in hand the faithless lover who had deserted his betrothed.

Twilight was creeping over the two castles. On the narrow ground separating the forts the brothers strove together in a deadly fight.

They were equally courageous, equally strong those two opponents, and their swords crossed swiftly, one in righteous anger, the other in wounded pride. But soon the elder received a blow, and the blood began to drop on his breast-plate.

The bushes were at this moment suddenly pushed asunder, and a maiden, veiled in white, dashed in between the fighters thrusting them from each other. It was Angela, who cried out in a despairing voice:

"In God's name stop! and for your father's sake cease, ere it be too late. She for whom you have drawn your swords, is now going to take the veil, and will beg God day and night to forgive you, Conrad, for your falseness, and will pray Him to bless you and your brother for ever."

Both brothers threw down their arms. Conrad, his head deeply bowed, covered his face with his hand. He did not dare to look at the maiden who stood there, a silent reproach to him. Henry took the weeping girl's hand.

"Come sister," said he, "such faithlessness does not deserve your tears."

They disappeared among the trees. Silently Conrad stood gazing after them. A feeling which he had never known seemed to rise up in his heart, and, bending his head, he wept bitterly.

IV.

The cloister, Marienburg, lay in a valley at some distance from the castles, and there Angela found peace. A wall was soon built up between the two forts Sternberg and Liebenstein, a silent witness of the enmity between the two brothers.

Banquet followed banquet in the newly built castle, and the beautiful Grecian won great triumphs among the knights of the Rhine.

But sorrow seemed to have taken possession of Sternberg castle. Henry had not wished to move the maiden from her purpose, but from the time of her departure, his strength faded away. At the foot of the mountain he caused a cloister to be built, and a few months later he passed away from this world, just on the same day that the bells were tolling for Angela's death.

The lord of Liebenstein was not granted a lasting happiness with his beautiful wife. She fled with a knight who had long enjoyed the lavish hospitality at castle Liebenstein. Conrad, overcome by sorrow and disgrace, threw himself from a pinnacle of the castle into the depths below.

The strongholds then fell into the hands of Knight Brömser of Rüdesheim, and since that time have fallen into ruins. The church and cloister still remain in the valley, and are the scene of many a pilgrimage.

Rhens

THE EMPEROR WENZEL

In the middle of a beautiful meadow at
Rhense near Coblentz stands the famous histori-
cal "king's chair". Here, where the lands of the
three great prelates of Cologne, Mayence and
Treves join together, the princely Seven met to
choose the new ruler who was to direct the
destiny of the Holy Roman Empire.

Here Charles IV. was chosen by the free will
of the Electors; here also the Seven elected
Wenzeslaus of the house of Luxemburg, Charles'
son, emperor. During his life-time Charles had
exerted himself very much over the election of
his first-born son, and he even made a pilgrimage
with him to Rhense on the Rhine where, at the
renowned "Königsstuhl," the chancellor of the
kingdom, Archbishop of Mayence, often held important conferences with their Graces of Treves
and Cologne, and the Count Palatine.

This Wenzeslaus of Bohemia had a great
predilection for the Rhine and its wines, and
later on, when, less by his own merits, than by

the exertions of his father and the favour of the electors, he became German emperor, his brother inheriting the sandy country of Brandenburg, he had even then paid more honours to the Rhine wine than any other of its lovers. It afforded him a greater pleasure than the enjoyment of wearing a crown. Finding that a good drink tasted better at the place of its origin, he often visited the brave Count Palatine of the Rhine who dwelt in this blissful country, and who had more casks in his cellar than there are saints' days in a year.

This proof of imperial confidence was by no means disagreeable to the very noble Elector Ruprecht of the Palatinate, and he neglected no opportunity of striving to ingratiate himself more and more into the emperor's favour.

Gallant Ruprecht would not unwillingly have exchanged his little Palatinate crown for an imperial one. Sometimes when his royal guest, becoming very jovial from the wine he had taken, confessed that the high dignity of emperor was becoming troublesome to him, the count agreed with him frankly, and never failed to let his imperial master know that the electors were discontented at his careless administration, and would be well pleased if he retired. Emperor Wenzel listened to all he said with perfect indifference, continuing in the meantime to revel in his wine.

One day the emperor was sitting with his gay companions at the Königsstuhl in Rhense. They were all very merry, as the cup of Assmannshäuser wine had already been passed round many times. This delicious vintage was very pleasing to Wenzel, and the other drinkers could not find words enough to praise it.

While the goblets were being handed round, and sounds of joviality filled the royal hall, the emperor stood up suddenly and, addressing himself to the count, said in a very light-hearted tone.

"I think the crown which was set on my head would not be entirely unbecoming to you. Well, I offer it to you, if you are able to place before me and my companions here, a wine which tastes better than this Assmannshäuser."

There was a cunning twinkle in the count's eyes as he beckoned to his page. After a while a servant rolled in a great cask, from which the cups were at once filled. The count stood up and presented the first goblet to the emperor.

"That is my Bacharacher wine, noble lords. Taste it; I can wait for your judgment without fear."

They all drank, and every face beamed with pleasure. The opinions were undivided in favour of the fiery Bacharacher. The emperor rose and loudly declared he preferred it to the Assmannshäuser. He could not praise it too highly, nor drink enough of it.

"This wine is worth more than a thousand crowns!" said he, enthusiastically. Wenzel kept his word and ceded his crown to Ruprecht of the Palatinate who, in his turn, made the emperor a present of six waggon-loads of Bacharacher wine.

*

THE TEMPLARS OF LAHNECK

On the opposite side of the Rhine from Coblenz, and towering above Lahnstein, rises Castle Lahneck, a keep shaped somewhat in the form of a pentagon. Lahneck succumbed to the hordes of Louis XIII. in the same year as the castle of Heidelberg was destroyed. The following stirring tale is associated with Lahneck.

It was the Templars of Jerusalem who erected this fortress whose imposing watch-tower rises nearly 100 feet above the main building. The riches of the Templars led to their destruction. The contemptible French king, Philip the Fair, by making grave complaints to the Pope obtained an order for the abolition of this much-abused order, and dragged the Grand Master with fifty of his faithful followers to the stake. Everywhere a cruel policy of extermination was immediately adopted against the outlawed knights, the chief motive of the persecutors being rather a desire to confiscate the rich possessions of the Templars than any religious zeal against heretics and sinners.

Peter von Aspelt, Archbishop of Mainz, had cast envious eyes on proud Lahneck which sheltered twelve Knights-Templar and their retainers. Alleging some faulty conduct on the part of the soldiers of the cross, he gave orders that the castle should be razed, and that the knights should exchange the white mantle with the red cross for the monk's cowl, but to this the twelve as knights *sans peur et sans reproche* offered a stout defiance. This excited the greed and rage of the archbishop all the more. From the pontiff, whom with his own hands he had successfully nursed on his sick-bed at Avignon, Peter von Aspelt procured full power over the goods and lives of the excommunicated knights of Lahneck. He then proceeded down the Rhine with many vassals and mercenaries, and presented the Pope's letter to the Templars, at the same time commanding them to yield. Otherwise their castle would be taken by storm, and the inmates as impenitent sinners would die a shameful death on the gallows. The oldest of the twelve, a man with silvery hair, advanced and declared in the name of his brethren, that they were resolved to fight to the last drop of their blood, and further, that they were quite prepared to

suffer like their brethren in France. And so the
fight between such fearful odds began. Many
soldiers of the Electorate fell under the swords
of the knights and their faithful servants, but
ever the furious archbishop ordered forward
new bands to fill the gaps. Day by day the
ranks of the defenders became thinner. Pro
minent everywhere in this hand to hand struggle
were the heroic forms of the twelve Templars, in
white mantle with blood-red cross. At last, at
a breach which had been defended with leonine
courage, one of the noble twelve sank beneath his
shattered shield, and closed his eyes in death.
A second shared his fate, then a third. The
others, bleeding from many wounds and aided by
the sorely diminished remnant of their retainers,
redoubled their brave efforts, but still death
wrought havoc in their ranks. When, on the evening of the day of fiercest onslaught the victorious
besiegers planted their banner on the captured
battlement, the silver-haired veteran, the former
spokesman, stood with blood-flecked sword
among the bodies of his fallen comrades, the
last survivor. Touched by such noble heroism
the archbishop informed him that he would be
allowed to surrender; but calling down the curse
of heaven on worldly churchmen and their greed
for land, he raised on high his sword and rushed

upon his foes. Pierced with many wounds the last of the twelve sank to the earth, and over the corpse of this noble man the soldiers of Mainz pressed into the fortress itself.

Peter von Aspelt preserved Lahneck as a place of defence and residence for an officer of the Electorate of Mainz, and nominated as first holder of the post, Hartwin von Winningen. The castle remained in the possession of the Electorate of Mainz for 300 years, but the sad story of the twelve heroic Templars is remembered in the neighbourhood of Lahneck to this day.

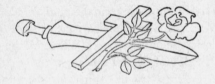

RIZA

In the first quarter of the 9th century, when the pious Ludwig, son of Charlemagne, was struggling with his misguided children for the imperial crown, a church was built in Coblenz to St. Castor, the missionary who had spread christianity in the valley of the Moselle. The four-towered edifice arose on a branch of the Rhine.

The palace of the Frankish king stood at this time on the highest south-western point of Coblenz, on the site of a former Roman fort, and near by was a nunnery, dedicated to St. Castor. In this building lived Riza, a daughter of Ludwig the Pious, who had early dedicated her life to the church. Every day this king's daughter went to mass in the Castor church on the opposite side of the Rhine. Such great grace had Riza found in the sight of Our Lord, that like His disciple of old on the sea of Genesareth, she walked over the Rhine dry-footed to the holy sacrament in St. Castor's. One day, the sacred legend goes on to say, the stream was agitated by a storm. For the first time doubt entered the maiden's heart as her foot touched the waves. Prudently tearing a prop from a neighbouring vineyard, she took it with her for a staff over the troubled waters. But after a few timid steps, she sank like St. Peter on the Galilean lake. In this wretched plight she became full of remorse for her want of faith in God. She flung the stick far away, and lifting her arms towards heaven, committed herself to the sole protection of the Almighty. At once she rose up from the waves, and arrived, with dry feet as heretofore, on the other side. More than ever after this did Riza, this saintly daughter of a saintly king, strive to excel in those works which are pleasing to God. She died within the cloister, and her bones were laid in the Castor church, near the burial-place of the saint. Soon the popular imagination canonised Riza, and her marble tomb is still to be seen in the North transept of the Castor church at Coblenz.

*

THE DOCTOR'S WINE OF BERNKASTEL

The wine of Bernkastel is called "Doctor's wine", or even shorter still. "Doctor," and it has been known by this singular name for more than five hundred years.

About the middle of the fourteenth century Bishop Bohemund lay ill of a very violent fever at Bernkastel. The worthy man was obliged to swallow many a bitter pill and many a sour drink, but all without avail. The poor divine began at last to fear the worst. Despite his high calling and his earnest search after holy things, his bishopric on the lovely Moselle pleased him better than any seat in heaven. He caused it to be proclaimed throughout the length and breadth of his diocese, that whoever should be able to cure him of this terrible fever, be he layman or learned doctor, should receive his pastoral blessing, and a rich present into the bargain.

At that very time, a brave old warrior lived at Treves, who heard about the suffering bishop and had pity on him in his great need.

Moreover this gray-haired veteran, whose name has not come down to posterity, was very much indebted to the bishop, for once, many years before, Bohemund had saved him from the hands of the enemy in a skirmish near Sponheim.

The noble old soldier was much distressed to hear that the holy man was suffering so terribly. He remembered too, that once he himself had been attacked by violent fever and had fought hard with death, and that his friends had talked about pills and certain bitter drinks, but he had sent them all away and had called his servant, desiring him to bring him a good bowl of fiery Bernkastler wine. When he had taken a hearty drink, — no small matter for one lying ill of fever — he awoke out of a deep sleep twelve hours later, the fever completely gone.

Why should not this same Bernkastler cure, thought he, have the same effect on the worthy prelate?

After considering for a time, the old knight set out quite alone from his castle in the forest of Soon to visit his spiritual benefactor, taking only a little cask with him.

Bohemund, lying on his sick bed, is said to have cast a very suspicious look at the good man who stated that he could cure him, but who carried all his medicines and mixtures in a little cask on his shoulder. The knight however, making a sign to the officious servants and attendants to leave the chamber, informed the reverend gentleman of what he was about to do. He then calmly took the plug out of the cask, and gave the sick man a drink of the sparkling wine which he had brought with him.

The bishop readily swallowed the wine at one draught. Another was administered to him soon after, and the eminent prelate fell into a deep sleep.

The next day the people of Treves heard with great joy that the fever had completely disappeared.

The bishop on awaking took another stout draught, and sang out of the depths of his grateful heart: —

> "This famous wine restored my health,
> Sure, 'tis a splendid doctor."

GENOVEFA

I.

In all the Rhine provinces the virtuous spouse
of Count Siegfried of the Palatinate was esteemed and venerated. The people called her St. Genovefa, which name indeed she was worthy of,
as she suffered cruel trials and sorrows. Siegfried's castle stood near the old town of Andernach, just at the time when Charles Martel was
reigning over the Franks.

Siegfried and his young wife lived in peaceful
unity, till a cloud came over their happiness. The
much-dreaded Arabs from Spain had forced their
way into Gaul, and were now marching north-
wards, burning and destroying all on their
course. The enemies of the cross must be repulsed,
unless the west was to share the fate of Africa,
which had been subdued by the Mohametans.

The war-cry reached the Palatinate, and Siegfried had to go forth to the fight. Equipped in
his armour, and having kissed his weeping wife,
he bade farewell to the castle of his fathers. But

he was sad at heart at leaving the spot where the happiest days of his life had been spent. He entrusted the administration of his property to Golo, his steward, and recommended his beloved wife very earnestly to his protection, begging her in turn to trust him in everything.

The poor countess was heart-broken at this bitter separation. She felt the loneliness of the castle deeply, she longed for his happy presence and the sound of his voice. She could never speak to Golo as to the friend to whose care her husband had recommended her. Her pure eyes shrank from the passionate look which gleamed in his. It seemed to her that he followed her every movement with a look which her childike soul did not understand.

She missed her husband's presence more and more. She would go out on the balcony and weave golden dreams, and while she sat there, looking out over the hazy blue distance, she longed for the moment when Siegfried would return, when she could lean her head upon his breast, and tell him of the great happiness in store for them.

Perhaps the war against the heathens might last so long that she would be able to hold the pledge of their love joyfully out to him from the balcony on his return. And the countess' lovely face would be lit up with a gleam of blissful happiness, and she would while away the time on her favourite spot, dreaming and looking out into the hazy blue distance.

The secret aversion which the countess felt towards the steward was not without a reason. Her angel-like beauty had awakened lustful passion in Golo's breast, which he did not strive to hide. On the contrary his frequent intercourse with her, who was as gracious to him as to all her other inferiors, stirred his passion still more, and one day, losing all control, he threw himself at the countess' feet, declaring his love for her, and imploring her to return it. Genovefa was horrified at this confession. With indignation and scorn she rejected his love, forbidding him to appear before her as he had utterly forgotten his duty, and at the same time, threatening to complain of him to her husband. Golo's eyes flared up, and a deadly look of hatred gleamed from them.

He could hope for no pardon from his angry mistress. Besides, his pride would not allow him to seek it, and now his one desire was revenge. It only remained for him to follow his dastardly plan and to avoid Siegfried's wrath.

Hatred raged in his breast. He dismissed all the servants of the castle and put new ones of his own creation in their places. Then one day he appeared before the horrified countess, and openly accused her of being unfaithful to her husband far away.

Shame and wrath robbed Genovefa of speech. Golo explained to the servants who were standing around in silent amazement, that he had already informed the count of his wife's faithless conduct, and that he, Golo, as present administrator of the castle, now condemned the countess to be imprisoned in the dungeon.

The unhappy Genovefa awakened to find herself in an underground cell of the castle. She covered her face in deep sorrow, imploring Him who had sent her this trial, to help her in her present affliction. There after some time a son was born to her. She baptized him with her tears, giving him the name of Tristan, which means "full of sorrows."

II.

Siegfried had already been absent six months. He had fought like a hero in many a desperate battle. The fanatical followers of Mohamet having crossed the Pyrenees, struggled with wild enthusiasm, hoping to subdue the rest of western Europe to the doctrines of Islam by fire and sword. In several encounters, the Franks had been obliged to give way to their power. These unbridled hordes had already penetrated into the heart of Gaul, when Charles first appeared and engaged the Arabs in the bloody battle of Tours. From morning till evening the struggle on which hung the fate of Europe raged. And there Charles proved himself worthy of the name of Martel "the hammer", which he afterwards received.

Siegfried fought at the leader's side like a lion; but towards evening a Saracen's lance pierced him, and though the wound was not mortal, yet he was obliged to remain inactive for several months on a sick-bed, where he thought with longing in his heart of his loving wife by the Rhine.

A messenger arrived one day at the camp bearing a parchment from Golo, Siegfried's steward. The count gazed long at the fateful letter, trying to comprehend its meaning. What he had read, ran thus: "Your wife is unfaithful to you and has betrayed you for the sake of Drago, a servant, who ran away." The hero crushed the letter furiously in his hand, a groan escaping from his white lips. Then he started off accompanied by a few followers, and rode towards the Ardennes, never stopping till he reached his own fort. A man stood on the balcony, looking searchingly out into the distance, and seeing a cloud of dust approaching in which a group of horsemen soon became visible, his eyes gleamed triumphantly.

A stately knight advanced, his charger stamping threateningly on the drawbridge. Golo, with hypocritical emotion stood before the count, who had now alighted from his foaming horse, and informed him again of what had happened. "Where is the evil-doer who has stained the honour of my house, where is he, that I may crush his life out?" cried Siegfried in a fury.

"My lord, I have punished the wretch deservedly and lashed him out of the castle," answered Golo in a stern voice, sighing deeply.

The count made a sign to Golo whose false eyes gleamed with devilish joy, to lead the way.

Siegfried entered the dungeon, followed by his servants and also by those who had travelled with him. Genovefa listened breathlessly in her prison, with a loved name trembling on her lips and a prayer to God in her heart. Now the terrible trial would come to an end, now she would leave this dungeon of disgrace triumphantly, and exchange the crown of thorns for the victor's wreath.

The bolt was unfastened firm steps and men's voices were heard, the iron doors were dashed open. She snatched her slumbering child, the pledge of their love, and held it towards her dear husband. His name was on her lips, but before she could utter it, a cry of agony escaped her. He had cast her from him and, his accusations falling like blows from a hammer on her head, the poor innocent countess fell senseless to the ground. The next day two servants led mother and child out into the forest, where with their own hands, they were to kill her who had been so unfaithful to her husband, and her child also. They were to bring back two tongues to the count as a proof that they had obeyed his orders.

The servants drove them into the wildest depths of the forest where only the screams of birds of prey broke the silence. They drew their knives. But the poor countess fell on her knees, and holding up her little child, implored them to spare their lives, if not for her sake, at least for the sake of the helpless child. Pity entered the two men's hearts and withheld their hands. Dragging the mother and child still deeper into the forest, they turned away hastily, leaving their victims to themselves.

They brought two hart's tongues to the count, informing him that they had fulfilled his orders.

III.

Genovefa's tired feet wandered through the unknown forest, her child crying with hunger. She prayed fervently to Heaven in her despair, and tears were sent to relieve the dull pain in her heart, after which she felt more composed, and her child was soon sweetly slumbering. To her great astonishment she perceived a cavern near her, where she could take shelter, and as if God wished to show that He had heard her prayer, a withe doe came towards the cavern, rubbing herself caressingly against the abandoned woman. Willingly the gentle animal allowed the little child to be suckled. The next day the doe came back again, and Genovefa thanked God from the depths of her heart. She found roots, berries, and plants, to support herself, and every day the tame doe came back to her, and at last remained always with her.

Days, weeks, and months passed. Her unfaltering faith had rendered her agony less. In time she learned to forgive her husband who had condemned her unjustly, and she even pardoned him who had taken such bitter revenge on her. Her lovely cheeks had become thinner, but the forest winds had breathed a soft red into them, and the child who had no cares nor gnawing pain in its heart, grew into a beautiful little boy.

IV.

At the castle on the Rhine, sorrow was a constant guest since this terrible event had happened. Siegfried's burning anger had sunk into sorrow, and often when he was wandering restlessly through the rooms so rich in sweet memories, where now a deserted stillness reigned, the agony awoke again in his heart. He now repented of his hastiness, and a voice whispered in his ear that he had been too severe in his cruel punishment, that he had condemned too quickly, and that he should have considered what he could have done to mitigate her punishment.

When these haunting voices pursued him, he would hurry away from the castle and its loneliness, not being able to bear the torment of his thoughts. Then to forget his trouble, he would follow the chase with the yelping hounds. But he only seldom succeeded in dulling his misery. Everywhere he seemed to see the pale face of a woman looking imploringly at him.

The state of his master's soul had not escaped Golo, and this crafty man fawned the more on the sorrowful count, feigning to care for his

welfare. A starving pers on accepts even the bread which a beggar-man offers, and Siegfried, supposing his steward wished to compensate him for his loss, accepted willingly every proof of devotion, and recompensed him with his favour, at the same time hating the man in his inmost soul who had rendered him such a terrible service.

One day the count rode out to the chase, accompanied by only a few retainers, one of whom was Golo. Siegfried pressed deeper than was his custom into the forest. A milkwhite doe sprang up before him and sportsmanlike, he chased this singular animal through the bushes, hoping to shoot it. His spear had just grazed it, when it disappeared suddenly into a cavern. A woman whose ragged garments scarcely covered her nakedness, leading a little boy by the hand, suddenly came out of the opening in the rock, and the doe, seeking protection, rubbed herself against her. She looked at the hunter, but her limbs trembled so that she could scarcely stand, only her large sad eyes gazed wistfully at him. A stifled cry, half triumphant, half a groan, escaped from her lips, and she threw herself at the count's feet. From the voice which for long months had only moved in earnest prayer or in low sweet words to the child, now flowed solemn protestations of her innocence. Her words burned like fire into the soul of the count, and drawing her to his breast, he kissed her tears, and then sank at her feet imploring her pardon.

He pressed his little boy to his heart, overcome with gratitude and happiness, and wept with joy, calling him by a thousand affectionate names.

Then at the sound of his bugle-horn his retinue hastened towards him, Golo among them.

"Do you know these two?" thundered out the count to the latter, tearing him from the throng and conducting him to Genovefa.

The wretch, as if struck by a club, broke down and, clasping his master's knees, he confessed his wickedness and begged for mercy. Siegfried thrust him contemptuously from him, refusing sternly, in spite of the countess' intercession, to pardon his crime. Golo was bound and led away, and a disgraceful death was his reward.

———

Now began a time of great happiness for Siegfried and his saint-like wife, and they lived in undisturbed peace with their little son.

In gratitude to Heaven Siegfried caused a church to be built on the spot where the white doe had appeared to him first. The countess often made a pilgrimage to this house of God, to thank Him who had caused her tears to be turned into joy. Then a day came when her corpse was carried into the forest, and was buried in the church. Even now in Laach, the wanderer is shown the church and the tombstone, also the cavern where she suffered so much. Thus the name of St. Genovefa will last for all time.

*

THE OLD KNIGHT
AND HIS DAUGHTERS

Above Rheinbrohl, on a dreary sandstone rock, stand the ruins of the old imperial fortress of Hammerstein. For a thousand years the storms have beaten on those desolate walls. One of the first owners was Wolf von Hammerstein, a faithful vassal of the Emperor. It was Henry IV. who then ruled, and partly through his own fault, partly through that of others, the crown had indeed become to this sovereign one of thorns. Wolf of Hammerstein had made the historic pilgrimage to Canossa alone with his master. Now, on account of the infirmities of age the venerable knight seldom descended the castle-hill, and only from afar, the loud trumpet call of the world fell upon his ears. His wife, now for several years deceased, had born him six daughters, all attractive maidens and tenderly attached to their surviving parent, but their filial affection met with the roughest and most ungrateful responses from the sour old fellow. It was a sore grievance to Wolf of Hammerstein that he had no son. He would willingly have exchanged his half-dozen daughters for a single male heir. The girls were only too well aware of this fact, and tried all the more, by constant love and tender care to reconcile their ungracious parent to his lot.

One evening it thus befell. The autumn wind was grumbling round the castle like a croaking raven, and the old knight, Wolf of Hammerstein, was sitting by a cheerful fire and peevishly nursing his gouty limbs. In spite of the most assiduous attentions of his daughters he remained in a most surly mood. The pretty maidens however kept hovering round the ill-tempered old fellow like so many tender doves. Then the porter announced two strangers. Both were wrapped in their knightly mantles, and in spite of his troubles the hospitable lord of the castle prepared to welcome his guests. Into the comfortable room two shivering and weary travellers advanced, and as outlaws they craved shelter and protection for the night. At the sound of one of the voices the knight started up, listening eagerly, and when the stranger raised his visor and threw back his mantle, Wolf of Hammerstein sank on his knees at the stranger's feet, and seizing his hand he pressed it to his lips, exclaiming:

"Henry, my lord and king!" Then, with trembling voice the Emperor told his old comrade-in-arms that he was a fugitive, and before one who had torn from him the imperial crown and mantle. And when the old knight, trembling with excitement, demanded who this impious and dishonourable man might be, the Emperor murmured the words, "My son," and then buried his face in his hands.

Rigid as a marble statue stood the old knight Like a bolt from heaven the consciousness of his past ignoble conduct had flashed upon him. Suddenly he seemed to feel how tenderly the loving arms of his daughters had enfolded him. He spread out his hands towards them, as if anxious to atone by the tenderness of a minute for the harshness of years. Then the Emperor, deeply touched, thus addressed the old man. "Dear comrade-in-arms, your position is indeed enviable. The faithful love of your daughters will tend you in your declining years. No misguided son, impatient for your end, will hunt you, from your home. Alas, for me, to-morrow accompanied by a few faithful followers, I must go down to battle against my own flesh and blood."

Towards midnight the unhappy monarch was conducted to a room prepared with care for his

reception; and, while he sank into a troubled
sleep, the old knight overwhelmed his daughters
with long-delayed caresses. In his heart, he
silently entreated for pardon for the deep grudge
he had long cherished against the God who had
been pleased to grant him no son.

*

Valley of the Ahr

THE LAST KNIGHT OF ALTENAHR

Only a few mouldering ruins now show where one of the proudest strongholds of the Rhine country, Castle Altenahr, once stood. A legend relates the mournful story of the last of the race which had lived there for centuries.

This man was a very stubborn knight, and he would not bow down to or even acknowledge the all-powerful archbishop, whom His Majesty the Emperor had sent into the Rhine country as protector of the church.

Unfortunately the bishop was also of a proud and unyielding character, and he nursed resentment in his heart against this spurner of his authority.

It was not long before his smouldering rancour blazed into an open feud, and the mighty bishop, accompanied by a large band of followers, appeared before the proud castle of Altenahr. A ring of iron was formed round the offending vassal's stronghold.

But its owner was not disturbed by this formidable array and only laughed sneeringly at the besiegers' vain efforts, knowing well that they would never be able to storm his rocky stronghold.

The warlike priest saw many of his little army bleeding to death in vain. He was very wrathful, but nevertheless undismayed.

He had sworn a great oath that he would enter this invincible hold as a conqueror, even if the fight were to last till the Judgment Day; the lord of Altenahr had sworn a similar oath, and these two powerful foes were well matched.

Thus the siege continued for some months. The besieger's anger grew hotter, for every attack cost him the lives of numbers of his followers, and all his efforts seemed useless.

Already there was an outburst of discontent in his camp; many servants and vassals deserted from such a dangerous venture. Revolt and disobedience seemed on one occasion to threaten a complete dissolution of the besieging army, as a desperate attack had been again repulsed by the hidden inhabitants of the fort.

The bishop's allies urged the unrelenting man to desist from his merciless purpose, but he received their protests with a sneer: „When you leave me, my greater ally, hunger, will draw near. It will come, that I am sure of." Then followed an uproar of confused voices; mutinous troopers, now become bold by the wine they had taken, fell to brawling with their leader. The bishop's grim smile died away.

"Wait my men, just wait for one more attack," he cried in a powerful voice, "it will be the fiercest and the last", and with a dark face the turned and strode away.

———

Dawn was creeping over the valley of the Ahr. There was a great stir in the camp on the side of the mountain, and up above, in the castle of Altenahr, silence reigned round the hazy pinacles. Suddenly a flourish of trumpets was heard, and the drawbridge having been let down, the lord of the castle galloped forth on a milk-white charger, his tall figure towering over the animal, the feather of his helmet waving above his grey hair, and the first rays of the rising sun irradiating his steel armour.

Holding his steed with a firm grip, he raised his right hand to the shouting besiegers, signifying that he wished to speak. His voice sounded far and wide.

"See here the last man and the last charger of all those who lived in my tower. Hunger has snatched them all from me, wife, child, comrades.

They all preferred death to slavery. I follow them, unvanquished and free to the last."

The noble animal reared up at the spur of its rider . . . . . a great spring, followed by a thundering crash . . . then the Ahr closed her foaming waters over man and steed.

A shudder seized those who were looking on. The dark countenance of their leader became pale as death, and he rode off without a moment's delay, followed by the curses of his mutinous troops.

Since that time the castle of Altenahr has remained deserted; no one dared to enter the chambers hallowed by the memory of this heroic defence. Thus it was avoided by mankind, till time gnawed at its walls and destroyed its battlements.

*

THE MINSTREL OF NEUENAHR

He was called Ronald, this tall handsome man, with blue eyes and fair hair; he had a noble bearing and was a master of song.

The knight at the Castle of Neuenahr had made a great feast, and Ronald was sitting on the drawbridge playing his harp and singing. The guests stopped their noisy conversation within doors, and knights as well as noble ladies listened breathless to the unseen singer. The proud lord of the castle bade his page bring the traveller in. Thus the tall handsome man, the blue eyed, fair-haired stranger with the noble bearing, appeared before the high company. The knights looked at him with wonder, and many a handsome lady covertly regarded him with admiration.

Among the high company there was a beautiful young girl, the daughter of the knight, whose birthday was being celebrated. The lord of the castle rose from his richly carved stool, and made a sign to the singer who was bowing graciously to the knights and ladies and lower still to the master of the castle.

"Give us a song, musician, in honour of our child who is seventeen years old to-day."

The musician fixed his glance in silent admiration on the maiden. She dropped her eyes, and a lovely blush covered her cheeks. He seized his harp, and after a few chords, began to sing a song of homage. Sweetly sounded the music, and even sweeter the flattering words. The maiden flushed a deeper crimson and cast down her eyes. Once when the harper in his song compared her to a star lighting a wanderer's path, she glanced up, and their eyes met; but hers sank quickly again. She seemed to waken out of a dream when the song ended amid loud applause. She saw her father lifting up a massive goblet and handing it to the singer, saw how the latter raised it first to her, afterwards to her father and his guests, and then put it to his own lips. The maiden felt she was no longer mistress of her heart which was beating as it had never done before.

II.

"You might teach my Rothtraut to play the harp," cried the proud lord of the castle, who was in a very lively humour, having partaken freely of wine. She heard it as in a dream, and the musician bowed, murmuring that he was not worthy to receive so signal an honour.

He remained however at the castle. Lovely Rothtraut felt afraid in her heart like a trembling child crossing a bridge leading to flowery meadows; she had no mother in whom she could confide those fears for which she could find no words. She therefore yielded to her father's desire, wishing to amuse him during the long, lonely evenings by playing and singing. Singing came naturally to her, for a nightingale seemed to slumber in her bosom, but she found more difficulty with the harp. Her slender fingers drew many a discordant sound from the strings, and often her father, comfortably seated in his armchair, laughed heartily at her, which made the maiden blush with shame. Her large eyes would wander from the harp to the musician's face; but her confusion only became worse when her eyes timidly met his. He was very patient with all her imperfect efforts, never blaming her but on the contrary praising all her modest attempts beyond their merits. Then he would sing a song of his own and play some deep chords which seemed to thrill the air. The knight would listen entranced, and the maiden felt love's blissful pain in her heart. She did not know what it was, or how he had long since sung himself into her soul, and her tender heart trembled at love's first revelation. The passion possessed her more and more; it spread its power over these two hearts, and soon in the quiet garden of the castle, Ronald clasped the daughter of the proud knight to his heart.

III.

Love's first rapture is often followed by sorrow however, and beautiful Rothtraut had yet to experience it.

It once happened that the knight surprised his child in the musician's arms. His anger knew no bounds, and like a beast of prey he rushed at the singer, when his daughter, suddenly become a woman, placed herself bravely between her father and her lover. Her confession went to his heart like a dagger, for with trembling lips and glowing cheeks, the maiden acknowledged the secret of her love.

Pale but firm the singer stood before the knight.

" I am only a wanderer but not a dishonourable one. Do not destroy with a rough hand the flower which God has planted in our hearts, but give me time. I will set out on my journey and will take up arms for my beloved. And when I come back as a nobleman, you will give me your daughter who loves me. Either I shall return as a knight, or you will never see me again."

The lord of the castle looked at him sternly, while his daughter stood weeping, holding Ronald's hand. "Good-bye, maiden. Do not forget me, Rothtraut!" He was gone, and a wailing cry burst from the lips of the unhappy girl.

IV.

To atone for many a wrong against Pope and Church, and also to fulfil a solemn vow, the Emperor Barbarossa started on a crusade in his old age. Many knights and heroes joined him, and his great army marched through several countries until they came to the Levant. Then they journeyed on to Syria where the great hero's career ended. Barbarossa was drowned, and the eyes of his followers turned to Henry, his son, as their leader. The latter, who became emperor under the name of Henry VI. was a very capable general; he was also a lover of music, and is said to have composed many a melody which remains with us to the present day.

Many supposed that it was not the royal minstrel who composed the songs, but that they came from the hand of Ronald who was now as skilled with his sword as with his harp, and who had become a great favourite of the emperor. He was a powerful warrior, and had already overthrown many a Saracen. Once when the crusaders had gained a glorious victory, he composed a song in honour of it, and sang it himself on his harp. The song went the round of the camp, and the singer became a great friend of the emperor. But even such favour did not drive the shadow from Ronald's soul, and often when he was singing one of his most beautiful songs to Henry, he would suddenly break off and rush out of the tent in great grief. One day the emperor found out what he had long guessed, and made Ronald confess his story to him.

Some days afterwards the crusaders began the storming of Acre, the impregnable fortress of the Saracens. Ronald was fighting by Henry's side. A Saracen dashed his falchion at the king's head, but Ronald with a mighty blow clove the infidel's skull in two. In the evening of the same day Henry called all his warriors together, and dubbed the brave champion knight with his own hand. Ronald of Harfenstein was to be his name, and a lyre lying on a falchion and a sword, were to be his arms. The emperor promised to build him a castle on the borders of the Rhine, which was to be called Harfeneck.

Plague broke out in the camp, and many a gallant crusader fell victim to it. Among them was the emperor himself, whose death caused unspeakable grief to Ronald.

V.

One day a weary crusader was seen riding along the banks of the Rhine. Wherever he passed, the people asked him if it were true that Barbarossa was not drowned in the Holy Land, but was living in the Kyffhäuser Mountain, and would soon come back to his own neglected kingdom. The crusader barely answered their questions, but urged on his tired steed along the Rhine. At last the silvery waters of the Ahr appeared before him, and he saw the gables of the castle. The rider joyously spurred on his horse, and rode up through the forest to the fortress where once he had sat on the drawbridge as a poor traveller.

The late guest was ushered up to the lord of the castle.

The knight, now a bent old man, rose from a melancholy reverie to greet the unknown stranger.

"I am Ronald, and have become a knight through the grace of the Emperor Henry in the camp at Acre, and now I have come to win your daughter Rothtraut."

"Win her from death, for it robbed me of her two months ago," said the proud lord of the castle, turning his head aside in deep grief. Then a despairing groan thrilled through the chamber. Harsh words passed between those two, one a man in his disconsolate sorrow, the other a repentant father.

Ronald strode off to the lonely corner of the garden, and the newly dug up earth showed him the place where Rothtraut lay. There he remained late into the night, till darkness had surrounded him and black night had settled on his soul. Then he turned and went away, never to come back again.

In the East whence the crusaders had now returned, everyone talked of the heroic deeds accomplished by Richard the Lion-hearted. The Saracens well knew the fearless leader and the German knight who fought at his side. Richard valued his bravery, even though he was still a young knight. He meant to make him one of his vassals when he returned to his own country. But his desire was never fulfilled, for the thrust of a hostile lance which he had so often escaped, pierced the knight's heart. So the minstrel of Neuenahr found a grave in the Holy Land; the race of Harfenstein became extinct with the first of the line, and the castle was never built.

*

THE BUILDING OF THE MINSTER

As Charlemagne, the mighty ruler of the Franks, rode one day from his stronghold at Aix-la-Chapelle into the surrounding forest, his horse is said to have suddenly trodden upon a spring. On touching the water, the animal drew its foot back neighing loudly as if in great pain.

The rider's curiosity was aroused. He alighted, and dipping his hand into the spring, found to his surprise that the water was very hot. Thus Charlemagne, as the legend records, discovered the hot spring which was to become the salvation of many thousands of ill and infirm people.

The pious emperor recognised in this health-giving spring the benevolent gift of Providence, and he resolved to erect near the spot a house of God the round shape of which should remind posterity of the horse's hoof.

The building was soon begun, and Charlemagne saw with great satisfaction the walls of the new minster rising high into the air. He was not however destined to see its completion. When he died, he had to leave the great Empire of the West to a feeble son. Lewis the Pious. The latter was compelled to draw his sword against his own children in order to assure for himself the crown he had inherited.

Many a great undertaking that Charlemange had begun, remained unfinished.

The building of the minster too was interrupted. The ground was left desolate, and the walls and towers were threatened with decay before they were finished.

It was quite useless for the honourable magistrate of the town to apply for money to the charitable Christian inhabitants. Contributions came in very slowly, and were never sufficient to finish the church.

The aldermen of Aix-la-Chapelle would very often seriously debate the question, and discuss how the could remedy the grievous lack of money and successfully effect the completion of the minster. They found however that good counsel was just as rare as building material.

Once when they were met thus together, a stranger was announced who said he had most important news to communicate. He was allowed to enter the session room. After having duly saluted the Council, he said modestly but without any shyness, "Gentlemen, my business, in a word, is to offer you the money for the completion of the church." The worthy aldermen looked in wonder first at the speaker, then at each other.

They silently agreed in the opinion that the man before them looked very suspicious in his quaint outlandish clothes and his sharp pointed beard.

But the newcomer was not at all abashed by their suspicious looks. On the contrary he repeated politely but firmly his proposal, saying: "Honourable Sirs, I should like to help you out of your difficulty, and will advance you the necessary thousands without even wishing to be paid back."

At this frank offer the councillors pricked up their ears and opened their eyes wide in astonishment. Before they could recover from their amazement, the stranger continued: "I know well, you are all far too proud to accept this great offer of mine without giving me a reward of some sort. Therefore I require a small compensation. I demand the first living being, body and soul, that enters the new minster on the inauguration day."

On hearing this the honourable aldermen rose horrified from their seats. Many of them made the sign of the cross or uttered a short prayer, because nobody but the devil himself could require anything so monstrous.

The eyes of the chairman shot a reproachful glance at the strange speaker, and he muttered between his teeth: "Be off! your words are giving offence."

But Master Satan, the stranger, stood calmly in his place: "Sirs", said he, "let me answer you with a word from the scriptures, "Why are you so fearful, oh ye of little faith?" On the field of battle the sword mows down thousands of brave men. They fall often as victims to the ravening ambition of a single man. You can even see fathers fighting against their sons, brothers against their brothers, and nobody thinks it unjust. Now you cry out, when I only ask for one single living soul to be sacrificed for the welfare of the whole community."

The eyes of the stranger looked round in triumphant joy when he had finished, for he read a favourable reply in the puzzled faces of the aldermen.

Many of them at once abandoned their scruples, and after a few minutes even the most cautious among them had no more objections to urge.

So they closed with the offer, and Master Satan left the Town Hall with a proud smile.

The next day the council was again gathered together anxiously waiting for the promised sum.

It arrived promptly, rightly weighed and in good honest coin.

The joy of the aldermen was boundless.

Once more the workmen began the work of building the minster. They worked very busily as if to make up for the long interruption, and after three years the cathedral was finished.

On the day when the new church was to be consecrated, a great festival was held in the town.

The distinguished company, secular as well as clerical, who appeared at the inauguration ceremony, praised the magnificence of the minster, the great liberality of the citizens, and more than all, the wisdom of the Town Council.

The aldermen listened to the general praise with pleasure, and accepted it as their due. They felt however bound to confess to each other that they did not feel easy when they thought of the inauguration day. None of them had spoken to anybody of Master Satan's condition.

Only one of them, a henpecked fellow as malicious people said, confessed the whole transaction to his wife. It is needless to say that from that moment the whole town knew about the affair. On the important day of the consecration of the minster many venerable prelates, abbots, and monks, thousands of noble knights and lords who had come as guests, and the whole population of Aix-la-Chapelle looked forward to the fatal hour with beating hearts. It was a grand procession indeed that marched on in ceremonious pomp through the streets. The gaily coloured flags waved merrily in the air, the trumpets and clarions sounded cheerily. The nobility and clergy were in their most gorgeous attire. On every side were the signs of joy and thanksgiving.

But the hearts of the people were all oppressed, and many a sorrowful eye gazed at the morning sky, as if expecting to see Satan flying down with his bat-like wings.

When the aldermen in their bright robes joined the procession, the general anxiety rose to the highest pitch.

Before the worthy councillors a bulky cage was carried by four stout footmen. What was hidden under the covering nobody knew, but everybody felt sure that it contained the victim.

179

When the procession reached the minster it stopped, the cage being carried in front.

At a sign from the mayor, one of the footmen quickly stripped off the cover and exposed to view a howling hideous wolf. Two of the men pushed the church door wide open with their long halberds, and the fourth pushed the wolf skilfully through the open door. A terrible noise arose suddenly within.

The devil had been waiting for his spoil, as a tiger that watches for his prey.

When the wolf entered the devil darted towards it, but seeing that it was only a beast he burst into a wild howl of rage.

He wrung the poor wolf's neck with the quickness of lightning and disappeared suddenly, leaving nothing behind him but a strong smell of sulphur.

A few minutes later the bells rang, and the whole magnificent procession thronged into the church, duly to celebrate its consecration.

While divine service was being held in the new minster, and hymns of praise and thanksgiving were offered at God's altar, the devil flew with horrible maledictions over the country.

He swore an oath to punish with the utmost

severity the population of Aix-la-Chapelle who had so cunningly outwitted him.

In his flight he came to the sea-shore where he stopped a little, in order to consider how he could best destroy the town. As he looked at the sandy dunes the thought struck him, that he might bury the whole town with all its prelates and abbots under such a hill. With a mighty pull he tore one of the dunes from the shore, piled it on his shoulders, and flew rapidly towards the doomed city. But the way was much longer than Master Satan had thought. He began to perspire very freely under his unwonted burden, and when from time to time the wind blew a rain of loose sand into his eyes, he swore most horribly.

In the valley of the Soers not far from Aix-la-Chapelle he was obliged to rest, as he was very tired after his exertions.

While he was thus sitting by the wayside wiping his forehead and looking hot and weary, a wrinkled old woman came limping along, who looked with suspicion at the man and his strange burden.

She wanted to pass by without saying a word, but the stranger stopped her and said: "How far is it from here to Aix-la-Chapelle?" The woman cast a sharp look at the speaker.

As she had reached years of discretion, being now in her seventy-second year, she was shrewd enough to recognise in the man before her the very devil in person. She was also quite sure, that he must have some wicked plan in his head against the good town, Aix-la-Chapelle.

Therefore assuming a very sad expression she answered in a complaining voice: "Kind sir, I am so sorry for you, the way to the town is still very long. Only look at my boots, they are quite worn from the long way, and yet I got them new from the shoemaker at Aix-la-Chapelle."

Master Satan uttered something that sounded like a bitter curse. Then he shook off the sandy dune from his shoulders and flew away in a fury.

The old woman was for a moment terror-stricken, but when she saw the fatal figure of the stranger disappearing, she was inexpressibly glad at having saved the town and outwitted the devil himself.

If he had only looked a little more carefully he could have seen the tower of the new minster not a mile off.

The sandy dune is still lying in the very same place where the devil dropped it. Its name is "Losberg" or "Ridmountain," so called because the town Aix-la-Chapelle got rid of a great danger.

The memory of the poor wolf is also still preserved. Its image is engraved on the middle of the minster door, where you can also see the big cracks produced by the devil's hammering it in his impotent anger.

*

THE RING OF FASTRADA

This story too leads us back to the time of the great Emperor Charles, whose life has come down to us with a halo of glory.

Charlemagne's favourite residence was Aix-la-Chapelle, but he also held court in Helvetia. His imperial stronghold stood on the shores of the Lake of Zürich. In its neighbourhood there was a high pillar which the emperor had erected to mark the place where Felix and Regula had died as martyrs to the Christian faith. A small bell was attached to this monument, which everybody in distress and want might ring if they wanted relief. Whenever Charles held his court in Zürich he himself appeared at the pillar when the bell was rung, and listened to the complaints and petitions of his subjects.

One day the sound of the bell was heard, yet nobody could be perceived near the pillar. On the following day about dinner-time the same thing happened, the bell rang, yet no one was there. The emperor, curious to know what this meant, commanded one of his pages to hide in the bushes behind the pillar.

When mid-day approached the boy noticed that a serpent crept out of the sand, wriggled up to the pillar, and set the bell a-ringing. This astonishing fact was at once communicated to the emperor, who came without delay to the spot. He was very much surprised at seeing such an unusual applicant, but he said with great earnestness, "Every one who comes to me shall find justice, be it man or beast."

The serpent went low before the monarch, and then crept back into its den. Charlemagne followed, anxious to learn the reason of its strange behaviour. He was surprised when, on looking into the dark hole, he saw an ugly toad sitting on the serpent's eggs, and filling nearly the whole space with its hideous form.

The emperor bade his attendants kill the intruder at once.

In a short time Charlemagne had nearly forgotten the strange incident.

But one day when he was sitting at dinner the serpent unexpectedly entered the hall, and crept up to the emperor's seat. Bowing low three times it lifted its head and dropped a precious stone into the emperor's goblet. It then disappeared as quickly as it had come.

Charlemagne took the stone out of the cup, and saw to his amazement that it was a precious diamond. He ordered it to be mounted in a golden ring, which he presented to his well-beloved wife, Fastrada.

The jewel possessed a wonderful quality. Fastrada had always been loved tenderly by her imperial husband, but after the diamond ring adorned her slender finger, a sweet charm seemed to bind her still more strongly to him.

To many people this great love of the emperor for his wife seemed too absorbing, almost superhuman, and when death ruthlessly snatched her from the side of Charlemagne, everybody believed that it was a judgment from heaven.

The monarch was inconsolable at this great bereavement. He spent days and nights in unspeakable grief by her corpse. The rumour was, that his sorrow was so intense that he refused to permit the remains of his wife to be duly buried. The charm the living Fastrada had exercised over him seemed to linger even after her death.

The Archbishop of Rheims, the pious Turpin, heard of the emperor's sorrow, and he offered fervent prayers to God for help. Soon afterwards he had a strange dream. He saw the wonderful ring on Fastrada's finger glittering with a thousand lovely colours and surrounding the emperor with a magic light. The bishop was now sure that the precious stone was the cause of the superhuman love the emperor bore to his wife.

On the following day before sunrise Turpin, the venerable old bishop, got up and went into the room where Charlemagne had again spent a night in bitter grief by the remains of his beloved wife. He was kneeling by the uncovered bier in fervent prayer when the bishop entered. Turpin went straight up to the body, and making the sign of the cross he took the cold waxen hand of Fastrada for a moment in his. Without being observed by the mourning emperor, he slipped the enchanted ring gently from her finger. As he had guessed the emperor at once rose, and kneeling down before the bishop, kissed his hand in adoration. Then he rose and bade Turpin have the remains of his wife buried that same day. So it happened that Fastrada's remains were brought to their last resting place in the Church of St. Albans at Mayence.

From that time the emperor was attached with rare devotion to the old Archbishop of Rheims.

He would not allow him to leave his side, but requested that Turpin should always live near him. The pious man was also nominated first councillor of the Empire.

Turpin used his high position only for the welfare of the empire, and did a great many good works.

Sometimes however he felt a pang of regret at the manner in which he had acquired the high favour of his lord, and it seemed to him very unfair.

Once when he accompanied the monarch on one of his journeys in Western Germany, he threw the ring into a spring from which it could never more be brought up again.

From that moment Charlemagne felt himself irresistibly drawn to that particular part of his extensive dominions.

He erected a stronghold there, and a flourishing township soon surrounded this palace. Later on it was called Aix-la-Chapelle, and became the favourite residence of the great emperor.

Within its walls he liked best to rest from the burden of affairs of State, and sometimes the old ruler could be seen sitting by the margin of the spring in which Fastrada's ring lay buried, recalling the sweet memories of past days.

KNIGHT ROLAND

The Emperor Charlemagne was surrounded by a circle of proud knights, the flower of whom was Count Roland of Angers, nephew of the King of the Franks. The name of no knight was so famous in battle and in tournaments as his. Helpless innocence adored him, his friends admired, and his enemies esteemed him. His chivalrous spirit had no love for the luxuries of life, and scorning to remain inactive at the emperor's court, he went to his imperial uncle, begging leave to go and travel in those countries of the mighty kingdom of the Franks, which up to that time were unknown to him. In his youthful fervour he longed for adventures and dangers. The emperor was much grieved to part with the brave knight, but however, he willingly complied with his request.

One day early in the morning the gallant hero left his uncle's palace near the Seine, and rode towards the Vosges Mountains, accompanied by his faithful squire. The first object

189

of his journey was castle Niedeck near Haslach, and from there he visited Attic, Duke of Alsace.

He continued his travels, and one evening as he was riding through the mountains, the glittering waters of the Rhine, washing both sides of the plain, greeted him. The river in that part of the country offered him few charms in its savage wildness, but he knew that the scenery would soon change. He moved on down the Rhine to where a gigantic mountain shuts the rushing current into a narrow space. Its foot stands chained in the floods, which only in places retire a little, thus leaving the poor folk a narrow stretch of land.

On the heights there were proud castles, telling the wanderer below of the fame of their illustrious races. Thus Roland made many a long journey on his adventurous course down the Rhine. He passed many a place rich in old memories: the Lorelei Rock, where the water nymph sang at night: the cheerful little spot where St. Goar lived and worked at the time of Childebert, the Merovingian, (that wonderful saint who once spread a fog over his imperial uncle, compelling him to pass the night in the open air, because his Majesty, while journeying from Ingelheim to Coblenz had neglected to bend his knee in his chapel) and the green meadows near Andernach, where Genovefa, wife of Palatine Count Siegfried lived. And now Roland neared the place where the stream reaches the end of the Rhine Valley, an where the seven giants are to be seen, the summit of one of which is crowned with a castle; there they stand like the seven knights who, in later times stood weeping round the holy remains of the German emperor.

A wooded island lay in the deep-blue waters. The setting sun threw a golden light over the hills. On the sides of the mountains there were numberless vineyards, to the left, hedges of beeches ascending to the heights of the rugged summits, to the right, the murmur of the rippling waters, and above, visible among the legendary rocks where once a terrible beast lived, the pinnacles of a knight's castle, and over all, the heavens clothed with a garment of silver stars.

The knight paused in silence; his glance rested admiringly on the beautiful scene. His steed pawed the ground uneasily with his bronze-shod hoofs, and his faithful squire looked anxiously at the darkening sky. He reminded his master modestly that it was time to seek shelter for the night.

"I should like to beg for it up there," said Roland dreamily, an inexplicable feeling of sweet sadness coming over him for the first time. He bade his squire ask the boat-man who was putting out his little bark to cross the river, what was the name of the castle? The castle was the Drachenburg, where Count Heribert sojourned sometimes. Thus ran the answer which pleased Roland very much. He had been charged with many greetings and messages to the old count at the Drachenburg from his friends living near the upper Rhine. Roland now hesitated no longer, and soon a boat was ploughing the dark waves.

II.

In the meantime night had come on. The full moon's soft beams showed them their way through the dark forest. Count Heribert, a worthy knight in the flower of his age, bade the nephew of his imperial master heartily welcome to his castle. Far past midnight they stayed in the count's chambers, engaged in entertaining conversation.

The next day Count Heribert presented his daughter Hildegunde to the knight. Roland's eyes, full of admiration, rested on the blushing young maiden. Never before had the charms of a woman awakened any deep feeling in his heart; he had only thirsted after glory and deeds of daring, after tournaments and feuds. Now the bold champion was struck with a shaft from the quiver of love. He who had opposed the dreaded adversary so often, now bowed his fearless head in almost girlish confusion before Hildegunde's charms. She, too, stood crimsoning deeply before the celebrated hero whose name was famous, and who was beloved in all the country round.

The old knight broke up the scene of embarrassing silence between the youthful couple with gay laughing words, and conducted his guest through the high halls of his castle.

Roland tarried longer at the friendly castle than he had ever done before in any other place in the country. He seemed bound to the blissful spot by love's indissoluble chains, and so it happened that one day these two found themselves hand in hand, the deep love in their hearts rushing forth in ardent words. Count Heribert bestowed his lovely daughter very willingly on the celebrated knight, his only desire being to complete the happiness of his child whom he loved so dearly. A castle should be erected for her on the heights of the rocks on the other side of the Rhine, opposite the Drachenburg, and this proud fort on the rugged rocky corner of the mountain, should be a watch-tower for the glorious Seven Mountains and their castle. In later times it became the famous Rolandseck. Soon the walls could be seen raising themselves up, and every day the lovers stood on the balcony of the Drachenburg looking across, where industrious workmen and masons were busily toiling. Hildegunde began to weave sweet dreams of the future round her new home, where she meant to chain the adventurous hero with true love.

But one day a messenger appeared at the Drachenburg on a horse white with foam. He was sent by Charlemagne and brought the tidings of a crusade which the emperor had decreed against the Infidels beyond the Pyrenees. Charlemagne desired to have the famous knight among the leaders of his army. Roland received the message of his great master in silence. He looked at Hildegunde who with a death-like face was standing beside him. Grief stabbed cruelly at his heart, but he must obey the call of honour and duty, and, informing the royal messenger that he would arrive at the imperial camp in three days, he turned sorrowfully away, Hildegunde sobbing at his side.

III.

The cross and the crescent were fighting furiously for the upper hand in Spain. Terrible battles were fought, and much blood flowed from both Christians and Infidels. Bloody victories were gained by the emperor's brave knights, the chief of whom was Roland. His sword forced a triumphant way for Charlemagne, it guarded his army, passing victoriously through the unknown country of the enemies. But the sad day of Ronceval, so often sung by German and other poets was yet to come. Separated from the main body of the army, Roland's brave rearguard was making its way through the dusky forest. Suddenly wild shouts sounded from the heights, and the cowardly Moor pressed down on the little band, threatening them with destruction. But the noble Franks fought like lions. Roland's charger, Brilliador, flew now here, now there, and many a Saracen was hewn down by its noble rider's sword, Durand. But numbers conquer bravery. The little army of Franks became less and less, and at last Roland sank, struck by the lance of a gigantic Moor. The combat continued furiously round him. When night spread mournfully over the battle-field, the Infidels had already done their terrible work. The Franks lay dead; only a few had escaped from the slaughter.

"Where is Roland?" was the frightened cry from pale lips. He was not among the saved. "Where is Roland?" asked Charlemagne anxiously of the messengers. Through the whole kingdom their answers seemed to resound, Roland the hero had fallen in battle fighting against the Saracens; wherever this cry was heard, it awakened deep sorrow.

The news soon spread as far as the Rhine, and one day the imperial messengers appeared at the Drachenburg, bringing the sad tidings and the deepest sympathy of the emperor. Heribert sighed deeply on hearing the news and covered his eyes with his hands; Hildegunde's grief was heart-breaking. Before the altar of the Queen of sorrows she lay sobbing her heart out, begging for comfort in her great need. For days on end she shut herself up in her little bower, and even her father's gentle sympathy could not assuage her bitter grief.

Weeks passed. Then one day the pale maiden entered the knight's chamber, her grief quite transfigured. He drew her softly towards him, and then she revealed the resolution which was in her heart. Count Heribert was overwhelmed with grief, but he pressed a loving kiss on her pure forehead.

The day came, when down below on the island Nonnenwert, the convent bells rang solemnly. A new novice, Count Heribert's lovely daughter, knelt before the altar. In the holy stillness of the convent she sought the peace which she could not find in the castle of her father. With a last great convulsive sob she had torn her lover's name from her heart, had quenched the flame of sorrowing love for him, and now her soul was to be filled ever with the holy fire of the love of God. In vain her afflicted father hoped that the unaccustomed loneliness of the convent would shake her resolution, and that when the first year's trial was over, she would return to him. But no! the pious young maiden fervently begged the bishop, who was a relative of her father's, to release her from the year's trial and to allow her after a short time to take her final vows. Her longing desire was fulfilled. After a month Hildegunde's golden locks were no more, and the lovely daughter of the Drachenburg was dedicated to the Lord forever.

IV.

Time rolled on. Spring had vanished and the sheaves were ripening in the fields. Where the river reaches the end of the Rhine valley crowned by the Seven Giants, a knight with his horse stopped to rest. Far away in the south, where the valley of Ronceval lies bathed in sunshine, he had lain in the hut of a poor herd. There the faithful squire had dragged his master pierced by a Morrish lance. The bold hero and leader had remained for weeks and months on his sick-bed struggling with death, till the force of his iron nature had at last conquered. Roland was recovering under loving care, while they were mourning him as dead in the land of the Franks. Then having recovered, he hurried back to the Rhine urged by an irresistible longing.

A wooded island lay in the deep-blue waters. The setting sun threw a golden light over the hills; numberless vineyards flanked the mountains, hedges of beeches were on one side, the murmur of waters on the other, and above the pinnacles of a knight's castle among the legendary rocks where once a terrible beast lived; over all the heavens clothed with a garment of silver stars.

Silently the knight paused, his glance resting admiringly on the beautiful picture. Now as in months before an inexplicable feeling of sweet sadness came over the dreamer.

"Hildegunde!" murmured Roland, glancing up at the starry heavens. Again as formerly a boat-man rowed across the stream, and Roland soon was striding through the forest towards the Drachenburg, accompanied by his faithful squire.

The old watchman at the castle stared at the late guest, and crossing himself, he rushed up to the chambers of his master. A man's figure, bent with age and sorrow, tottered forward. "Roland!" he gasped forth. The knight supported the broken-down old man in his arms. When Roland had departed long ago, his grief had found no tears; now they flowed abundantly down his cheeks.

The knight tore himself from the other's arms. "Where is she?" he asked in a hoarse voice, "dead?" Count Heribert looked at him with unspeakable sorrow. "Hildegunde, bride of Roland whom they supposed dead, is now a bride of Heaven."

The hero groaned alound, covering his face with his hands.

In spring he left the Drachenburg and went to the castle on the rocky corner, and there he laid down his arms for ever; his thirst for action was quenched. Day by day he sat over there, looking silently down on the green island in the Rhine, where the nun, Hildegunde, wandered about among the flowers in the convent garden every morning. Sometimes indeed it seemed that she bowed kindly to him, then the knight's face would be lighted up with a gleam of his old happiness.

But even this joy was taken from him. One day his beloved did not appear; and soon the death-bell tolled sorrowfully over the island. He saw a coffin which they were carrying to its last resting-place, and he heard the nuns chanting the service for the dead, he saw them all, only one was wanting . . . then he covered his face. He knew whom they were carrying tho the grave.

Autumn came, withering the fresh green on Hildegunde's tomb. But Roland still kept his watch, gazing motionlessly at the little churchyard, and one day his squire found him there, cold and dead, his half-closed eyes turned towards the place where his loved one was sleeping.

For many a century the proud castle which they called Rolandseck, crowned the mountain.

Then it fell into ruins, like the mighty Drachenburg, the tower of which is still standing. Fifty years ago the last arches of Roland's castle were blown down one stormy night, but later on they were built up again in memory of this tale of true and faithful love in olden times.

Siebengebirge

THE ORIGIN
OF THE SEVEN MOUNTAINS

In olden times the Rhine flowed into a deep mighty lake above the town of Königswinter. Those who then lived near the Eifel Mountains or on the heights of the Westerwald, were in constant fear of these swelling waters which often overflowed, causing great destruction in the country. They began to consider that some great saviour was necessary, and sent a messenger into the country of the Giants, begging some of them to come down and bore through the mountain, which prevented the waters from flowing onward. They would receive valuable presents as a recompense.

So one day seven giants arrived in their country, bringing enormous spades with them, and with a few good strokes of their tools, they made a gap in the mountain so that in a few days the water washed through the gap which visibly became larger. At last the river streamed through in torrents. The lake gradually dried up and completely disappeared, and the liberated Rhine flowed majestically towards the plain.

The Giants looked at their work with satisfaction. The grateful folk brought them rich treasures, which they had taken out of the mines. Having divided them fraternally, the Giants shouldered their spades and went their way. These heaps of rocky ground which they had dug out were so great, that ever since they have been called the Seven Mountains, and will remain there until the Giants come again and sweep them away.

*

THE DRACHENFELS

I.

When the wanderer has left the "city of the Muses," Bonn, he perceives to the left the mighty summits of the Seven Mountains. The rocky point of one these hills is still crowned by the tower and walls of an old knight's castle. A most touching legend is related of the mountain with the terrible name.

In the first centuries after the birth of the world's Redeemer, the Germans on the left side of the Rhine accepted willingly the doctrines of the Cross; Maternus, a disciple of the great Apostle, had brought them over from Gaul. At first the pious messenger of Christ worked among the heathen tribes in vain. They persisted in their paganism, and even prevented the priests from coming into their country.

At that time there was a terrible dragon living in the hollow of the rock which even now is called the Dragon's hole. He was of a hideous form, and every day he used to leave his den and rage through the forests and valleys, threatening men and animals. Human strength was powerless against this monster; the people thought that an angry deity had his abode in this terrible beast, so they bestowed godlike honours on him, sacrificing criminals and prisoners to him.

A tribe of heathens lived at the foot of the mountain. These men, desirous of war, often made raids on the neighbouring countries, carrying fire and sword among their Christian brothers. They once crossed the water, plundering the land and making prisoners of the people. Among the latter there was one most lovely maiden, whose beauty and grace inflamed two of the leaders so much, that each of them desired to have her for himself. One was called Horsrik the Elder, a famous chieftain, known to have the strength of a bear and the wildness of a tiger; the other, Rinbold, of a less rough nature, but of equal bravery.

The beautiful maiden turned aside shuddering when she saw the two chiefs' glaring eyes, contending for possession of her. All round were their men intoxicated with victory. The struggle for the Christian maid affected the two leaders more than the division of the booty. Soon the angry words of the two opponents found an echo in the hearts of the men standing round.

Horsrik, the much-feared figther, claimed her, and was received with cheers. Rinbold, the proud young chieftain, claimed her also, — great applause greeted him. The former glared sternly, grasping his club in a threatening manner. The high-priest, an old man with silver-white hair and stern features, stepped in between the two combatants, and in a voice surging with anger he said:

"Cursed be every dissension for the possess-ion of this stranger! A Christian must not disunite the noblest of our tribe. A daughter of those we hate, she shall fall to nobody's share. She, the author of so much strife, shall be sacrificed to the Dragon, and shall be dedicated to Woden's honour at the next rising of the sun."

The men murmured applause, Horsrik more than the rest. The maiden held her head upright Rinbold, the proud young chieftain, looked sor-rowfully at her angel-like face.

II.

Early the following day before the sun had poured his bright beams an the earth, the valley showed signs of life. Through the dusk of the forest a noisy procession moved upwards towards the highest point, the priest in the

middle, behind him the prisoner, pale but resolute. Silently, for her Lord's sake, she had allowed the priest to bind her forehead as a victim, and to place consecrated flowers in her loose flowing hair. Many a sympathetic look from the crowd had been cast at the steadfast maiden. The young chieftain was stricken with pain at the sight of her death-like countenance.

There stood the projecting rock which had often been dishonoured by human blood. The fanatical priests wound ropes round the maiden's body, and then tied her to St. Woden's tree which overhung the precipice. No complaint escaped the Christian's white lips, no tears glistened in her eyes which were glancing up at the morning sky. The throng of people moved off, waiting silently in the distance to see what would happen.

The first rays of the sun streamed over the mountain; they lighted up the wreath of flowers in the maiden's hair, playing about her lovely face, and crowning it with glory. The Christian maid was awaiting death, as a bride awaits her bridegroom, her lips moving slightly as in prayer.

A gloomy sound came up from the depths. The Dragon started from his den, spitting fire on his path. He cast a look at his victim there on the spot which his blood-thirsty maw knew so well. He raised his scaly body, thus letting his sharp claws be more visible, moved his snaky tail in a circle and showed his gaping mouth. Snorting the monster crawled along, shooting flames out of his bloodshot eyes.

A shudder of death crept over the maiden at the sight of this awful beast. Tremblingly she tore a sparkling golden crucifix from her breast, held it towards the monster piteously, and called on her Lord in a heart-rending voice. Wonder of wonders! Raising himself, as if struck by lightning, the monster turned, dashing himself backwards over the jagged stones into the waters below, and disappearing in the river among the falling rocks.

Wondering cries arose from the waiting heathens. Astonishment and wonder were depicted on every face. In quiet submission, her eyes half-closed, the maiden stood, praying to Him who had saved her. The cords fell from her sides; two strong arms caught her and carried her into the midst of the astonished crowd. She raised her eyes and perceived the younger of the two chieftains. His rough warlike hand had seized hers. The young man bent his knee as if to a heavenly being, and touched her white

209

fingers with his lips. Lord applause greeted him on all sides.

The old priest came forward, the people waiting in great expectation. "Who had saved her from certain destruction? Who was the God who so visibly aided His own?" asked he solemnly of the Christian. With bright eyes the maiden answered triumphantly:

"This picture of Christ has crushed the Dragon and saved me. The salvation of the world and the welfare of man lies in Him." The priest glanced at the crucifix with reverent awe.

"May it soon lighten your spirit and those of all these people round," said the maiden earnestly. "It will reveal greater wonders than this to you, for our God is great."

The maiden and all the other prisoners were conducted back to their own country. But the former soon returned again, accompanied by a Christian priest. The voice of truth and innocence worked wonders in the hearts of the heathens. Thousands were converted and baptized. The old priest and Rinbold were the first who bowed their heads in submission to the new doctrine. Great rejoicings were held among the tribe when the maiden gave her hand to the young chieftain. A Christian temple was erected in the valley, and a splendid castle was built on the summit of the rocks for the newly-married couple. For about ten conturies their descendants flourished there, a very powerful race in the Rhine countries.

*

THE MONK OF HEISTERBACH

In olden times in a lovely valley near the Seven Mountains, stood a cloister called Heisterbach. Even now parts of the walls of this old monastery remain, and it was not by the hand of time, but by the barbarism of foolish warfare, that its halls fell into ruins. The monks were driven away, the abbey was pulled down, and the stones were used for the building of a fortress.

Since that time, so the country folk relate, the spirits of the banished monks wander nightly among the ruins, raising mute accusations against their persecutors and the destroyers of their cells. Among them there was one, Gebhard, the last Prior of Heisterbach, who now, they say, wanders about the graves of the monks, and also haunts the burial-places of the Masters of Löwenburg and Drachenburg.

In the Middle Ages the monks of Heisterbach were very famous. Many a rare copy of the Holy Scriptures, many a highly learned piece of writing was sent out into the world from this hermitage, telling of the industry and learning of the pious monks.

There was one brother, still young in years, who distinguished himself by his learning. He was looked up to by all the other brethren, and even the gray-haired Father Prior had recourse to his stores of knowledge. But the poisonous worm of doubt began to gnaw at his soul; the mirror of his faith was blurred by his deep meditations. His keen eye would often wander over the faded parchment on which the living word of God was written, while his childlike believing heart, humbly submitting itself, would lamentingly cry out, "Lord, I believe, help Thoe mine unbelief!" Like a ghost his restless doubts would hover about him, making his soul the scene of tormenting struggle.

One night with flushed face he had been meditating over a parchment. At daybreak he still remained engrossed in his thoughts. The morning sun threw his bright rays over the heavens, casting playful beams on the written roll in the monk's hands.

But he saw them not, his thoughts were wholly taken up by a passage which for months past had ever been hidden to him and had been the constant subject of his reflections, "A thousand years are but as a day in Thy sight."

His brain had already long tormented itself over the obscure words of the Psalmist, and with a great effort he had striven to blot it out of his memory, and now the words danced again before his weary eyes, growing larger and larger. Those confusing black signs seemed to become a sneering doubt hovering round him: "A thousand years are but as a day in Thy sight."

He tore himself away from the silent cell, seeking the cool solitude of the cloister-gardens. There with a heavy heart he paced the paths, torturing himself with horrid doubts.

His eyes were fixed on the ground, his mind was far away from the peaceful garden, and without being aware of what he was doing, he left the cloister gardens and wandered out into the neighbouring forest. The birds in the trees greeted him cordially, the flowers opened their eyes at his approach; but the wretched man heard and saw nothing but the words: "A thousand years are but as a day in Thy sight."

His wandering steps grew feeble, his feverish brain weary from want of sleep. Then the monk sank down on a stone, and laid his troubled head against a tree.

A sweet, peaceful dream stole over his spirit. He found himself in spheres glowing with light;

the waters of Eternity were rushing round the throne of the Most High; creation appeared and praised His works, and Heaven extolled their glory; from the worm in the dust, which no earthly being has been able to create, to the eagle soaring above the heights of the earth: from the grain of sand on the sea-shore, to the gigantic crater, which, at the Lord's command, vomits fire out of its throat which has been closed for thousands of years: they all spoke with one voice which is not heard by the haughty, being only manifest and comprehensible to the humble. These were the words of Him who created them, be it in six days or in six thousand years, "A thousand years are but as a day in Thy sight."

With a slight shudder the monk opened his eyes.

"I believe Lord! help Thou my unbelief," murmured he, taking heart.

The bell sounded in the distance. They were ringing for vespers; sunset was already gleaming through the forest.

The monk hastily turned towards the cloister. The chapel was lighted up, and through the half-opened door he could see the brothers in their stalls. He hurried noiselessly to his place, but to his astonishment he found that

215

another monk was there; he touched him light-
ly on the shoulder, and strange to tell, the man
he saw was unknown to him. The brothers, now
one, now another, raised their heads and looked
in silent questioning at the new comer.

A peculiar feeling seized the poor monk, who
saw only strange faces round him. Growing
pale, he waited till the singing was over. Confused questions seemed to pass along the rows.

The Prior, a dignified old man with snow-
white hair, approached.

"What is your name, strange brother?" asked he in a gentle, kind tone. The monk was
filled with dismay. "Maurus," murmured he in
a trembling voice. "St. Bernhard was the Abbot who received my vows, in the sixth year
of the reign of King Conrad, whom they called
the Frank."

Incredulous astonishment was depicted on
the brothers' countenances.

The monk raised his face to the old Prior
and confessed to him how he had wandered out
in the early morning into the cloister-gardens,
how he had fallen asleep in the forest, and had
not wakened till the bell for vespers sounded.

The Prior made a sign to one of the brothers. Then turning to the monk he said: "It is

almost three hundred years since the death of St. Bernhard and of Conrad, whom they called the Frank."

The cloister annals were brought, and it was there found that three hundred years had passed since the days of St. Bernhard. The Prior also read the following note.

"A doubter disappeared one day from the cloister, and no one ever knew what became of him."

A shudder ran through the monk's limbs. This was he, this brother Maurus who had now come back to the cloister after three hundred years! What the Prior had read sounded in his ears as if it were the trumpet of the Last Judgment. Three hundred years!

With wide-open eyes he gazed before him, then stretched forth his hands as if seeking for help. The brothers supported him, observing him at the same time with secret dismay; his face had become ashy pale, like that of a dying person, the narrow circle of hair on his head had become snow-white.

"My brothers," murmured he in a dying voice, "value the imperishable word of the Lord at all times, and never try to fathom what he in His wisdom has veiled from us. May my

218

example never be blotted out of your memory. Only to-day the words of the Psalmist were revealed to me. "A thousand years are but as a day in Thy sight. May he have mercy on me, a poor sinner." He sank lifeless to the ground, and the brothers, greatly moved, repeated the prayers for the dead over his body.

THE HIGH CROSS AT
GODESBERG

If you walk on the high road between Bonn and Godesberg which is not far distant, you perceive on the left side, shimmering white amid the green woodland, a high pillar crowned with a cross known as the "High Cross".

It is a pleasing sight to him who passes by on a bright day; but in the twilight its glaring white contrasting so sharply with the dark background, makes a dismal impression on him, which is still more enhanced by the legend told about it.

The story leads us back to the time when instead of the grey ruins, a proud stronghold near Godesberg looked down into the wonderful valley of the Rhine. An old knight lived there, who was well known far and near for his bravery and generosity. His beloved wife had died, leaving him two sons.

The elder was the very image of his mother in body and mind; he had gentle child-like man-

220

ners, and it was therefore natural that the father's eye rested with more pleasure on him than on the younger son who was very daring, and in spite of his youth had already gone after strange, and not always honourable adventures. Yet the old father did not grieve much on his account, hoping that the sooner the reckless youth emptied his cup of pleasure, the sooner he would come to the bitter dregs. Then like others he would surely become more serious, and would yet fulfil the longing desire of his late mother. She had fervently wished to see him when a man, adorned with St. Matern's ring, which the bishops of Cologne wore, while Erich, the elder, should become lord of Godesberg Castle.

The father's thoughts lingered with pleasure on the pleasant prospects of his sons' future. He sent up many a fervent prayer to heaven for the fulfilment of his desires, well knowing that the spirit of his beloved wife supported him at the throne of the Almighty with her own supplications.

The old knight often spoke to his younger son about his vocation in life, but always observed with disappointment that his son avoided any allusion to the subject.

When the father felt his death approaching, he imparted once more his wish to his two sons, that the elder should become master of the castle, and the younger, bishop of Cologne. With a blessing for them on his lips, he closed his eyes for ever.

His death was sincerely deplored by all the poor people of the neighbourhood.

Some time after the two brothers sat as usual in the high banqueting-hall of Godesberg. It was a very dismal meal, for they sat opposite to each other, the elder with reproachful looks, the younger with knitted brows.

"I only took what the ancient law of my fathers bestowed upon me," said the elder mildly but firmly, in answer to some harsh words of his companion. "I am not master, but only manager of the family possessions. All our ancestors whose pictures look down on us in this hall would curse me, if I did not take good care of their legacy. But you, my dear brother, will receive a higher gift than a castle. You, the offspring of a noble race, shall become a worthy servant of our Saviour."

"Never!" burst forth the younger one in passionate eloquence, "never will I bow my neck to an unjust law that compels one to take up arms, and another meekly to accept a monk's cassock. If they offered me now a bishop's ring

222

or a cardinal's hat, I would not become a priest, I shall remain a knight."

The elder brother listened sorrowfully to this headstrong speech. "May God, whom you thus blaspheme, enlighten your dark heart. I would willingly share with you whatever I possess, but our father's will forbids it. Therefore bend your proud neck humbly, and beware of the judgment that will fall on him who despises the will of his dying father."

Hunting horns and trumpets sounded through the green forest which extended at that time from the town of Godesberg to the gates of Bonn. This huge wood abounded in noble game.

The two brothers were indulging together in the pleasures of the chase, as they had done so often in their father's life-time. Count Erich had gladly accepted his brother's invitation to accompany him.

He was only too glad to see how his dark mood had changed in the last few days and given way to greater cheerfulness. It appeared to Lord Erich as if his brother had come to reason, and after all had made up his mind to fulfil their parents' wish. He believed all the more in the happy change when he heard that his brother intended presenting himself to the Archbishop of Cologne, in order to deliver a letter of great importance from his late father to him.

Count Erich's heart was glad. He roamed joyfully through the forest, and his gladness seemed to increase his good luck in the sport. Several gigantic boars were pierced through by a spear sent from his hand. A deer also met with a similar doom.

The younger brother's success was on the contrary very meagre. His hand was unsteady and his whole bearing betrayed restlessness. A strange subdued fire gleamed in his eyes.

While he was following the trail of a mighty boar, Count Erich met him and offered to pursue the animal in his company.

They hunted through thorns and thicket, accompanied by the yelping hounds. Suddenly the foliage rustled, and the boar was seen to break wildly through the bushes. A spear from the younger brother whirred towards the beast, but missed its aim and remained sticking in the bark of an oak.

"Your hand is more fit to bless pious Christians," said Count Erich with a smile.

"But still fit enough to rid me of an inconvenient brother!" muttered the younger brother between his teeth, and tearing his hunting knife rapidly from his belt, he plunged the two-edged steel into his brother's breast. A terrible cry at the same time rang through the forest, and the murderer fled in haste.

Two attendants of the Count who were hunting close by, hearing the cry came running to see what was the matter, and found Lord Erich lying in his blood, dying. They bent down over him to se if they could help him, but alas! it was too late. The man, mortally wounded, was beyond the reach of human aid. With a last effort he opened his lips, muttered lowly but audibly the words, "My brother!" then sank back and closed his eyes for ever.

The terrible news that the Lord of Godesberg had been foully murdered by his own brother, spread swiftly through the country. Mourning again filled the castle on the mountain, when they carried the body of the poor slain man to his untimely grave. They buried him in the family vault next to the recent grave of his father.

From that time the castle stood desolate. The next relative of the noble family, who lived in a lovely part of the Rhine valley near the Palatinate, avoided a place where such an unheard of crime had been committed. Only an old man kept watch in the empty castle. But even he was soon compelled to leave it. One night the high tower was struck by lightning and the whole building burnt down. Nothing remained but blackened ruins, looking mournfully on the gay landscape beneath.

Years went by after this crime. Nobody heard or saw anything of the murderer. He seemed to have totally disappeared. Some people however whispered that on the day of the black deed, a man was seen fleeing from the forest of Godesberg. He was pale and ghastly looking, and darted off, not caring which way he went. It was he who on the previous day had fostered in his burning brain the longing desire to take possession of his brother's heritage, and now he was a murderer, and bore Cain's mark on his forehead.

The unfortunate youth had rashly contrived this hellish plan to rid himself of his brother and to become lord of Godesberg. His plan was to kill him while hunting, and then make the people believe that he had aimed at a boar and hit his brother accidentally instead. But when his victim sank down in agony, the knife dropped from his murderous hand, his courage failed him, and he felt himself driven from the wood as if chased by a demon.

226

After many years had come and gone, a tired wanderer once knocked at the door of the cloister of Heisterbach, which had been erected by St. Benedict's pious disciples in a remote valley of the Seven Mountains. The man who desired admission looked more like a beggar than a pilgrim. His garments hung torn and ragged round his thin body, and his face was deeply furrowed by marks of long and cruel suffering.

"Have pity on me," said he in a trembling voice. "I come from the Holy Sepulchre, my feet will bear me no further." The door-keeper was moved, and retired to inform the Abbot of the poor man's request. He received permission to bring him in. When the beggar appeared before the Abbot, he fell on his knees and renewed his demand for food and rest. For some moments the monk looked penetratingly at the man before him, then a sign of recognition passed over his face, and he cried out. "Good heavens! is it you Sir Knight?" The pilgrim trembled, prostrated himself before the Abbot, and embraced his knees in overwhelming grief. "Have mercy on me," exclaimed he, "it was I who twenty years ago slew my brother in the forest of Godesberg. For twenty long years I have tried to atone for my cursed deed and obtain forgiveness and peace. As a pilgrim I cried for mercy at the grave of him whom I murdered; as a slave of the Infidels, under the weight of heavy chains I prayed incessantly for God's mercy, but I cannot find peace. Three months ago the fetters were struck from my hands, and I have again come home, weary unto death. You, oh worthy Abbot, have known me from a child. Let me rest within the walls of this cloister, that I may daily see the castle where I was an innocent child. I will pray and do penance until death releases me from my wretched life."

The Abbot felt intense pity for the unhappy man. He bent down, laid his hands on him, and blessed him.

For many years the poor penitent remained in the cloister trying to atone for his crime with fervent prayers and hard penance. At last God in His grace called him away, and the repenting sinner died hopeful of Heaven's forgiveness. The monks buried him in a shady place in their cloister garden.

Bonn

THE ROMAN GHOSTS

Before the gates of the old Roman town of Bonn rises a mountain of moderate height, called Kreuz-berg, or "Crossmountain".

In early mediaeval times pious pilgrims went to this sacred place, in order to kneel on the holy steps of the old convent church so rich in memories of the martyrs, or to pray in the chapel. On the same spot at the beginning of the fourth century, the great saints of the Theban legion, Cassius, and his companions Florentius and Melusius, died for the Christian faith.

These martyrs were the guardian saints of the country round Bonn. Many a prayer sent up to them had graciously been fulfilled, since the time when St. Helena, the pious mother of Constantine, erected a chapel to their honour on Kreuzberg.

Once upon a time a simple peasant from the neighbouring country went on a pilgrimage to St. Cassius' burial place.

He came to ask the kind martyr for assistance in his distress. Dransdorf was his village, formerly called Trajan's village, because the general, who later on became Emperor Trajan, is said to have had a villa there.

A bad harvest had brought troubles on the peasant, but he firmly believed that through the intercession of St. Cassius he would receive money enough in one way or another to enable him to pay his many debts.

On arriving at Kreuzberg, he began his religious exercises by confessing his sins to one of the monks belonging to the order of St. Francis. Then according to custom he knelt in succession on one sacred step after the other till he reached the chapel. His wife had carefully put a candle in his pocket which he now lighted before the image of St. Cassius. Having thus fulfilled all the duties prescribed by the church, he turned homewards, well content with himself.

When he crossed the principal square of the town, where already at that time the magnificent Minster stood, he entered this church to pray once more, and to put another coin into the poor-box.

Twilight was creeping through the aisles, and a pilgrimage being not at all an easy thing, our peasant soon fell asleep over his prayer-book.

He only awoke, when somebody pulled him by his sleeve. It was the sexton with a big bunch of keys.

At first the peasant gazed drowsily at the unwelcome intruder, then with astonished eyes he looked round about him, until at last it dawned upon him, that the must get up and leave the church. Rousing himself he made the sign of the cross, and left the Minster with tottering steps. The night winds rustled in the old lime-trees of the square and seemed to whisper strange tales into the ears of the late wanderer.

The peasant crossed the open space sulkily, and steered his way towards the Sternthor, which led to Dransdorf. An ancient Roman tower, the remains of the high fortifications erected by the soldiers of Drusus eighteen hundred years ago, stands in the narrow lane, leading from the minster-square to the Sternthor. To the tired wanderer this tower seemed a splendid shelter, all the more so, as it would not cost him a penny.

He entered it, and tired out with the weary day, he was soon fast asleep as if he had never been stirred up from the bench in the Minster. No sexton with noisy keys was to be feared, and yet in his sleep the countryman had the sensation of somebody tapping him on the shoulder. He sat up and looked round. To his amazement he beheld a magnificent warrior standing before him, clad in a coat of mail with a Roman helmet on his head. Two companions in similar array stood by his side.

They nodded genially down to him, and it struck him that he had already seen them somewhere else. After some moments he remembered the pictures of St. Cassius and his friends in the chapel on Kreuzberg. There was no doubt the three holy martyrs stood in person before him.

Our good peasant was so much awed at this discovery that he could not utter a word, but at a sign from his mysterious visitors, he followed them at a respectful distance.

They marched towards the Sternthor, straight into the building, the walls of which were as thick as the rooms were long in the peasant's humble little cottage. In the middle of a high vault there was a table covered with sparkling gold.

At this unusual sight the peasant opened his eyes very widely indeed; but his astonishment changed into keen delight when one of his ghostly visitors filled his left pocket and another his right with the glittering metal. Meanwhile the third man took a tumbler from the middle of the table, and presented it to him with an encouraging smile.

He thought their language was very much like that which the vicar of the village church used in reading the service. Though the simple man could not understand a word of their conversation, he interpreted the kind invitation quite correctly, and shouting out a merry, "Vivat!" as a salute to his hosts, he emptied the tumbler at one big draught.

The whole building resounded with the echo, "Vivat!" The three warriors looked pleased and answered in a cheerful voice, "Vivat, Vivat!"

All at once it seemed to the peasant as if the vault was filled with a multitude of Roman soldiers who all called out to him, "Vivat!" as if happy to hear a sound of their native language in the country of the north.

The man from Dransdorf became quite high-spirited, and kept on shouting, "Vivat, Vivat!" Suddenly startled ly the noise he made, he awoke and found himself lying on the floor of the Roman tower in the Sterngasse.

The events of the night only seemed to him like a strange dream. But when he felt in his pockets he found them stuffed with real golden coins of a strange ancient stamp.

Our friend's joy became quite uproarious. After having sent up a heartfelt thanksgiving to St. Cassius, he gave vent to his delight by shouting through the quiet streets at the top of his voice, "Vivat, Vivat!"

A watchman stood on duty by the Sternthor, when the jocund peasant passed by. He made a step forward and, reaching out his arm, he gave the merry man a rude knock with his lance. Unmindful of this rough admonition, the peasant related the event in the Roman tower to the watchman, and finished his story by inviting the stern man of duty to an early draught at the nearest inn.

Rumours of the wonderful events spread far and wide, and soon every town and village knew the tale. The small lane leading from the Minster-square to the Sternthor was called "Vivat" lane, and bears that name to the present day.

Some years ago a heavy winter gale destroyed the old Roman tower that had so long withstood the vicissitudes of time. The people of Bonn however did not wish to obliterate the memory of this curious story, and therefore named the street running parallel with "Vivat" lane — "Cassius Graben."

RICHMODIS OF ADUCHT

It was about the middle of the fifteenth century.

The shadows of death hovered above the holy City of Cologne. A strange figure in dark garments hurried with quick steps through the streets and lanes. It was the plague. Its poisonous breath penetrated into cottages and palaces, extinguishing the lives of many thousands.

The grave diggers marked innumerable houses with a black cross, to warn the passers-by that the destroying angel had entered there. The roll of the dead rose to such numbers that it was impossible to bury them all in the customary manner. Therefore the bodies of the unfortunate people were thrown together into a common grave, covered only scantily with earth and marked with a plain wooden cross.

Woe and sorrow thus filled the old City of Cologne.

On the New-market, close to the Church of the Apostles, in a splendid mansion, the rich

Magistrate, Mengis of Aducht lived. Wealth could not save his house from the dreadful epidemic, his youthful and lovely wife, Richmodis, was seized with the plague and died. The grief of her lord was boundless. He passed the whole night by the remains of his beloved spouse, dressed her himself in the white wedding gown she had worn as a happy bride a few years before, decorated the coffin with sweet white flowers, and covered her with the precious jewels and costly rings she had loved so much. Then she was buried.

Night approached, and the clear starry sky looked peacefully down on the afflicted town. Perfect stillness prevailed in God's acre. — Suddenly a jarring sound like the opening of an old rusty lock was heard, and two dark shadows glided among the graves, on and on till they stopped before the fresh mould which enclosed the body of Richmodis of Aducht. — Those two knew the spot, and well they might, for they were the grave-diggers, and had prepared this grave themselves on the previous day.

They were present when the lid of the coffin was screwed down, and had with hungry looks coveted the glittering precious stones Richmodis was to be buried with.

Now they had come to rob the dead body. With spade and shovel the wreaths and flowers were quickly removed from the mound, the earth dug up and the coffin laid bare. In feverish haste, spurred on by their greed, they burst the lid open, and the dim light of their lantern fell full on the mild pale face of the dead woman. With haste the bolder of the two wretches loosened the white waxen hands folded together as in prayer, and tried to tear off the rings.

Suddenly the body quivered, and the white hands spread out. Aghast the robbers dropped their tools, scrambled in utmost terror out of the grave, and fled as if chased by the furies.

A painful long sigh rose from the depth of the grave, and after some time the white form of Richmodis who had been buried alive, emerged from the tomb.

With wide open eyes, full of horror, she look-ed down into the ghastly bed she had just left. — Could it really be true, or was it only a frightful dream?

God's acre was silent, but for the rustling of the autumn leaves of the weeping willows. Stillness of death everywhere! — No answer came to her faint cry for help — The horror of her situation however wakened her declining strength. She took up the lantern which the robbers had left behind them and with feeble steps reached the entrance of the churchyard.

The streets were desolate. The stars overhead alone perceived the slowly moving form, every now and then resting against the walls of the houses. — At last she reached the Newmarket and stood before the door of her home. Dark and quiet it seemed. But from the window in the magistrate's room a faint light shone forth. A quiver ran through the frame of the poor wife, and a wild longing desire seized her to be sheltered by his loving arms and to feel in his embrace that she had really returned to life again.

With a last effort she seized the knocker, and listened with newly awakened hope to the tapping sound which rang clear through the night.

A few minutes elapsed. Then an old servant peeping out of the window in the door, perceived the white ghostly figure of his late mistress. Horror seized him, his hair stood on end. Richmodis called him by his name and begged him to open the door. At the sound of her voice the old man started, ran upstairs, dashed into his master's room uttering incoherent sounds, and stammering: "O Lord, the dead rise; outside stands our good Mistress and demands entrance!" But the Magistrate shook his head in deep grief: "Richmodis, my beloved wife is dead and will never return, never, never," he repeated in unspeakable sorrow; "I will rather believe that my two white horses will burst from their halters in the stable and mount the stairs to the tower."

A terrible sound suddenly filled the quiet house, a noise like thunder was heard, and Mengis of Aducht and his servant saw the two white steeds tearing and tramping in haste upstairs.

A moment later two horses looked out of the tower windows into the night, and shortly afterwards the Magistrate laughing and crying with joy at the same time, held in his arms his wife who had returned from the grave.

For many years Richmodis lived happily with her husband, surrounded by several lovely children. Deep piety remained the motive power of Richmodis' being, and nobody ever saw her smile again.

If you come to Cologne, reader, you will still see the old house of the Aduchts at the Newmarket, with two white wooden horses' heads looking out of the top window.

THE CATHEDRAL-BUILDER
OF COLOGNE

It was at Cologne in the year 1248 on the eve of the Ascension day of our Lord.

Before the mighty Archbishop Kunrad of Hochstaden stood a simple architect offering the plan of a church, and arrogantly boasting that it would become one of the most beautiful cathedrals in Christendom. That man was Master Gerhard of Ryle.

The Archbishop was greatly astonished at the grandeur of the design, and ordered the execution of the bold plan without delay.

On the square which was selected for the erection of the new cathedral, another church had once stood during the reign of the first king of the Franks, but it had been destroyed by the Normans.

Now again gigantic masonry, slender pillars, bold vaults and arches rose to unite into a proud dome.

Everybody admired the humble man, whose creative genius now employed thousands of industrious workmen, and Master Gerhard's name was mentioned with great praise at home and abroad.

When the choir was finished, crowds of pious pilgrims came from the surrounding suburbs and even from a distance to pray before the relics of the three holy kings which were enshrined there. Hymns of praise re-echoed through the unfinished aisles.

Everybody rejoiced. But he, who ought to have been the most glad, was sad, and dark forebodings damped his spirits. The question if after all he would live to see his proud building finished, or if cruel fate would tear him away before he should have tasted the sweetness of triumph, tormented him day and night. His young wife saw with grief the change in his disposition; but she tried in vain by tender words and caresses to smooth his sorrowful brow.

The more he was troubled by his gloomy thoughts, the more he urged his workmen on. — Four years had elapsed; it was now 1252. The tower on the north side rose already proudly into the air. The scaffolding reached higher and higher every day.

One day Master Gerhard stood beside the big crane, watching how the gigantic blocks of stone taken from the quarries at the Drachenfels, were lifted up. He thought with pride and satisfaction that his work was going on well; and that he surely would see it finished. While thus meditating he did not observe that a stranger stood by his side watching him with an ugly sneer. A burning red cloak hung round his tall figure, a gold chain glittered on his breast, and a cock's feather nodded from a quaint velvet cap. He introduced himself to the somewhat surprised builder as a fellow-architect. "You are building a lovely church," he then said, "but I created a far more magnificent mansion, long long years ago. Its stone will never crumble to dust, and it will resist the influence of time and weather forever." In saying this, his eyes glittered strangely under his shaggy brows. This presumptuous speech did not please Master Gerhard, and without answering he measured the bold speaker scornfully from head to foot.

"Your church," continued the stranger, "will be a very lovely building, but don't you think that such an enterprise is far too audacious for mortal man. You, Master Gerhard, you ought to have known at the time when you laid the foundation stone of your church that you never would see your work finished."

"Who is likely to prevent it?" angrily burst forth the builder. No one had ever dared to use such language towards him, nor to wound his pride so keenly. "Death," coolly replied the stranger. "Never," cried Master Gerhard in a great fury, "I will finish what I began, and would even bet with the devil himself that I shall do so."

"Hallo!" laughed the stranger grimly. "I should like to deal with such an audacious man as you, and make bold to bet with you that I will, in a shorter space of time, finish the digging of a canal from Treves to Cologne, fill it with water, and have merry ducks swimming on it, than you will take to complete your church."

"So be it!" said Master Gerhard very much startled, taking the outstretched hand of the strange man. At the touch of his cold fingers, a sensation of horror crept into the heart of Master Gerhard. But the red-cloaked man burst into a yelling laugh and cried out in a formidable voice, "Remember we gambled for your soul." Utmost terror seized the trembling architect, cold perspiration stood on his brow, and he tried in vain to utter a word.

Suddenly a storm rose, the stranger unfolded his red cloak, and was lifted from the ground in a cloud of dust and vanished.

From that day the mind of Master Gerhard grew more and more gloomy. He kept on wandering restlessly on the scaffoldings of the building. The more he considered the huge dimensions of the cathedral, the more doubtful he felt as to whether he would be able to finish it or not.

By day-break he could be seen among his workmen, and till late in the evening he wandered about on the building-ground, praising the industrious and blaming the idle. He looked out anxiously sometimes in the direction of Treves to see if he could discern anything uncommon there. But he never saw the slightest change, nor any sign that the stranger with whom he had wagered, had really begun his canal in earnest, and he looked more hopefully into the future.

One day he was standing as usual on the top of one of the completed towers, when he felt a hand laid on his shoulder. Turning round, he beheld with disagreeable surprise the ghostly stranger. Was he a master of the black art or was he the devil himself? "Well, Master Gerhard," began the unwelcome visitor, "how are you getting on with your work? I see it is making good progress. Happily I shall soon have finished my canal, else I should run the risk of losing my bet."

"I can scarcely believe your boastful speech," answered the builder scornfully, "because I do not perceive the slightest trace of your having begun the canal," "Know, my dear man, that I am worth more than a hundred workmen together and, as I told you, my work is nearly ready," said the man in red.

"Really," said Master Gerhard a little startled, "I should like to know what magic power could enable you to do so."

"Come and follow me," replied the stranger, taking the builder by the hand. Off they flew through the air with the quickness of lightning, and reached the earth in the district near Treves in a few seconds. A the place where they descended, a spring arose from the ground and sent its crystal waters into an opening in a rock. "Come with me," said the magic stranger, and bending town he disappeared into this opening.

Master Gerhard followed him and came into a high glittering grotto, where he perceived that the water gushed tumultuously into the mouth of a black underground channel.

"You see," said the stranger, "how well I have used my time. If you have the heart for it, we will follow the waters, and see how far my canal reaches already."

Scarcely had he uttered these words, than a mysterious power seized both and pushed them forward with tremendous rapidity.

Master Gerhard saw now with terror that the work of the Evil One was indeed not far from its completion, for when they emerged from the dark canal, they had the City of Cologne lying close before them. The cathedral-builder could no longer doubt the great skill of his rival, and he felt sure that he would lose his bet. The red-cloaked man seemed to take great delight in the builder's discomfiture, and he said with an ugly grin.

"Well, Master Gerhard, I see you have found more than you expected. I am sure you would like to see the merry ducks which shall swim on my brook, according to our bet."

He clapped his hands three times and then listened. Some minutes passed, but no ducks appeared. The stranger's face assumed an expression of rage, when he found his summons unsuccessful. He tried again but in vain. After this he gave a frightful yell, and vanished all at once, leaving nothing behind him but a smell of sulphur.

The cathedral-builder had looked on in wonder, and new hope began to fill his heart, that after all he could win the wager.

"I know well, why the ducks wont appear," thought he, "but I shall never betray my secret to him."

246

After this adventurous journey, Master Gerhard was a prey to melancholy.

He was seen oftener than before on the building ground. It was impossible for him to doubt any longer, that the stranger with whom he had made the fatal bet, was the devil himself. The unfortunate man was well aware that not only was his life at stake, but that the salvation of his soul was likewise in danger, should the master of hell carry out his work.

There was only one little hope left for him, namely, that the devil would be unable to find out how to keep the ducks alive while they were swimming through the long underground channel. So Master Gerhard took courage, saying to himself: "He cannot win and I know why."

His young wife was strangely moved at her husband's silence and melancholy. She tried by increased tenderness and love to unstop his silent lips and to make him tell what was lying so heavily on his heart.

He appreciated her endeavours to cheer him very much, but could not be brought to tell of his dealings with the Evil One, and so he kept his secrets to himself.

One day, not long after the mysterious journey of Master Gerhard, a stranger, apparently a scholar, entered the architect's house, while he was as usual on the building ground. A scarlet cloak enveloped his tall figure, and a cock's feather sat boldly on his black cap.

His manners were soft and in general those of a gentleman. Hearing that the builder was not at home, he asked for his wife. She came and soon found that she liked talking to him, because he showed not only great eloquence, but also great sympathy for her husband.

Involuntarily she disclosed to the kind stranger her secret grief about Master Gerhard's sadness. The scholar listened to her troubles with great attention, and seemed to feel for her in her sorrow. "My dear Mistress," said he in a soft voice, there is surely some secret weighing heavily on his mind, and this and nothing else is the cause of his melancholy. Unless we know it, we cannot cure him. You are nearest to his heart. If you are very loving and tender to him, he will not withhold the secret for long from you. Be extremely kind to him. After three days I shall come back to see if you have been successful. If not, I will give you a remedy that will unfailingly make him tell you his inmost thoughts.

Thus speaking he took his leave, and she was unable to find words to express her gratitude.

For three days she tried the scholar's advice, but found that her husband, in spite of all her coaxing and caresses, would not tell the cause of his melancholy.

On the fourth day, the scholar called again and heard with apparent grief how badly her endeavours had succeeded, "I pity you heartily," said he, "but don't despair. Here is a wonderful herb. Prepare a beverage with it for your husband and make him drink it before he goes to sleep. He will dream after the draught and betray his secrets in his sleep."

She accepted the gift gratefully, and prepared the potion according to his advice. Her husband took the beverage willingly, and soon fell into a profound sleep. After some time dreams seemed to trouble him; he tossed restlessly to and fro in his bed murmuring incoherent words. His wife listened anxiously and heard in feverish excitement about the terrible dealings between him and the devil. After a pause Master Gerhard muttered:

"He will never win, because I hold the secre."

"What may that be?" she whispered in the dreamer's ear.

"He may do what he will," he answered unconsciously, "it is quite impossible that ducks should swim through the underground channel, unless he makes air-holes at every mile. Of course this idea will never come into his head."

The next morning the scholar called upon the wife and heard how well his scheme had succeeded. She told him everything. When she had revealed her husband's secret to him, the meek features of her strange guest suddenly changed. He gave a loud shrill scream of joy and disappeared. The poor wife remained on the same spot, pale and terror-stricken.

Master Gerhard was standing the next day by the high crane of the cathedral as usual.

The air was sultry, and black clouds were gathering from across the Rhine. He felt very restless, and urged his workmen even more than before to hurry on. The builder's heart was strangely filled with dark forebodings. All at once he felt an hand on his shoulder, and turning round, he beheld with terror the fatal stranger. A wondrous gleam of reddish flames seemed to radiate all round his figure.

The cathedral builder grew pale as death and trembled from head to foot. He was unable to utter a word.

Beaming with the joy of triumph, the Evil One pointed with his hand downwards, and forced Master Gerhard to look in the same direction. Behold! At the foot of the cathedral a silvery brook was visible running from the direction of Treves. Merry ducks were swimming on its shining surface.

It is impossible to describe the feelings of the builder at the sight of the completed work of his rival. Despair and agony made his heart sink within him, but the Evil One looked with joy on his victim. When he suddenly tried to grasp him, Master Gerhard darted to the edge of the scaffolding with a heart rending scream, and dashed himself down into the depths below, and was instantly killed.

A roar of thunder filled the air at that moment, and the devil vanished in a blaze of lightning. The thunder-storm grew more and more violent, After a few minutes the unhappy cathedral builder's house was struck by lightning and burnt to ashes in less than an hour. Unfortunately the admirable plan of the splendid church was also destroyed.

This was the sad end of Master Gerhard and his ambition.

The cathedral remained untouched for more than six centuries after. Its unfinished walls and towers began to decay as if they mourned the terrible death of their builder. The Cologne people believed for a long time that the spirit of Master Gerhard used to hover about midnight round the high towers and the desolated vaults. Strange sounds like the sighs of somebody in anguish were often heard in the deserted building, and people said it was Master Gerhard's ghost complaining that his proud cathedral remained unfinished.

Generation after generation passed by, and six centuries elapsed before busy workmen began again hammering and building on the ground which had lain so long quiet.

In 1880 the dome was finished, and towers now in all its majesty high above the dwellings of the people, and can be seen miles away.

Since that glorious day when the last stone was added to the cathedral of Cologne, Master Gerhard's ghost has never been heard or seen again.

THE GOBLINS

This story goes back to the "good old times" of which we modern people always speak with a sigh of regret.

It was then when good-natured goblins appeared to mortal eyes, and tried to render the life of the troubled human race a little more cheerful. In groves and dens they had magnificent dwellings and watched there over the enormous mineral treasures of the earth.

Often these beneficent elves were busy miners or sometimes clever artisans. We all know that they manufactured the precious trinkets and arms of the Nibelungen treasure.

Deep in the interior of the earth they lived happily together, ruled over by a king. They could be called the harmless friends of darkness, because they were not allowed to come into broad daylight. It they did so, they were transformed into stones.

The goblins did not always remain underground. On the contrary they often came to the earth's surface through certain holes, called goblin-holes; but they always avoided meeting man.

Alas! the advance of civilisation has driven these friendly spirits gradually from the places where they used to do so much good. None of us, I am sure has ever had the good luck of meeting one of them.

The goblins were of different sizes. Sometimes they were as small as one's thumb, sometimes as large as the hand of a child of four years old. The most remarkable feature of these tiny figures was the enormous head and the pointed hump that so often adorned their backs. Their look was on the whole more comical than ugly. German people used to call them "Heinzchen" or "Heinzelmännchen."

A long time ago the good town of Cologne was inhabited by a host of dwarfs, and the honest population knew a great many stories about them. The workmen and artisans especially had, through the assistance of the little wights, far more holidays than are marked in the calendar.

When the carpenters for instance were lying on their benches in sweet repose, those little men came swiftly and stealthily along, they took up the tools and chiselled and sawed and hammered with a will, and thus, records the poetical chronicles which I am quoting, before the carpenters woke up, the house stood there finished.

In the same way things went on with the

baker. While his lads were snoring, the little goblins came to help. They groaned under the load of heavy corn-sacks, they kneaded and weighed the flour, lifted and pushed the bread into the oven, and before the lazy bakers opened their eyes, the morning bread, brown and crisp, was lying in rows on the table.

The butchers too could speak of similar agreeable experiences. The good little men chopped, mixed and stirred with all their might, and when the drowsy butcher opened his eyes at last, he found the fresh, steaming sausages adorning the walls of his shop.

The cooper enjoyed also the help of the busy dwarfs, and even the tailor could not complain of the goblins having neglected him.

Once Mr. Cotton, a clever tailor, had the honour of making a Sunday coat for the mayor of the town. He worked diligently at it, but you can easily imagine that in the heat of the summer afternoon, the needle soon dropped from his hand, and he fell fast asleep. Hush! — look there. One little goblin after the other crept cautiously from his hiding place.

They climbed on the table and began the tailor's work and stitched and sewed and fitted and pressed, as if they had been masters of the needle all their lives.

When Master Cotton awoke, he found to his great joy the mayor's Sunday coat ready made, and so neatly and well done that he could present the magnificent garment with pride to the head of the town.

The pretty wife of Mr. Cotton looked at this master-piece of her husband's art with a mischievous twinkle in her eyes.

In the night when her husband had fallen asleep, she rose from her bed without making the slightest noise, and scattered pease all over the floor of the workshop; she then put a half-finished suit on the table. She kept a small lantern hidden under her apron, and waited behind the door listening. Soon after the room was full of little men all tumbling, falling, and slipping over the pease. Yells and screams rose at the same time. The poor little men were indeed much bruised and hurt. Without stopping they ran downstairs and disappeared.

The taisor's wife heard the noise, and thought it good sport. When the yells were loudest, she suddenly opened the door to see her visitors, but she came too late. Not a single goblin was left behind.

Since that time the friendly dwarfs have never more been seen in Cologne, and in other places also they have entirely disappeared.

JAN AND GRIET

"There lived at Cologne on the old farm of Kümpchenshof a peasant who had a maid called Griet and a man-servant called Jan."

Thus begins the old well-known Rhenish song of "Jan van Werth," the celebrated general of the imperial cavalry at the time when the Swedes and French were taking advantage of the civil war in Germany. But nobody except the inhabitants of the holy City of Cologne, knows that Jan van Werth was originally a simple labourer, and that he was indebted for his luck in life to his bad luck in love.

Jan was an industrious farmer boy with an upright character and a handsome face.

Many a girl would not have rejected him as a sweetheart, but Jan's tender heart had long been captivated by the good looks of pretty Griet, the comely maid of the Kümpchenshof. His love could not long remain a secret. One day he confessed to her with sobs that he loved her dearly, and would with pleasure work and toil for her twice as much as he then did for his master. He spoke long and earnestly, and taking courage with every word he uttered, he at last put to her the all important question — would she become his wife?

Laughingly the pretty girl put her round arms akimbo, tossed her head back and looked at her honest suitor with a mocking twinkle in her eyes. Then she shook her head energetically and said: "You are only a farmer's labourer, my dear boy, and will remain one most probably all your life. True, it is not your fault, but all the same I should prefer to marry a rich farmer with cows and oxen and horses."

Bitter anger rose in Jan's breast on hearing her talk so heartlessly, but he controlled himself. "Just as you like," he said sadly, and turned away from the haughty maid.

From that day he could not endure any longer the life at the farm, and pocketing his wages, he said good-bye for ever to the Kümpchenshof and became a soldier.

It was a furious war in which the German Emperor was engaged against the enemies of his country, and brave soldiers were rare. Any valiant warrior might distinguish himself and become an officer at that time.

The farmer-boy, Jan, soon won by his bravery and intrepidity the esteem of his superiors, and was promoted to the rank of colonel. Once when fighting against the Swedish troops he showed such determination and courage that he won the battle. After this brillant act he was made a general. But the name of Jan van Werth became even more famous when he beat the French in a skirmish at Tüttlingen.

In another way also his good luck reconciled him to the first bitter disappointment caused by Griet's scornful answer. He married a lovely and noble young lady, who was very proud of becoming the wife of such a celebrated general.

Let us now look back and see what happened in the meantime to Griet. She had waited month after month and year after year for the rich farmer. But the longed-for suitor never made his appearance. Even in those by-gone days red cheeks and bright eyes were much less thought of than ducats and glittering gold.

As time went on Griet grew old, and though she would now have been content with a simple man for her sweetheart, not even such a one condescended to ask her to become his wife.

Little by little Griet gave up all hopes of ever marrying, and had to look out for a living to keep her in her old age from starving.

Therefore she started a fruit stall at one of the large gateways of Cologne.

One day the good inhabitants of this town were in great excitement, and crowded in their best Sunday-clothes round the gate of St. Severin, where Griet sat at her apple-stall. They had come to meet Jan van Werth, the celebrated general, who was returning victorious at the head of his regiment.

There he was sitting on a powerful charger which was gorgeously covered with gilded trappings. On his fine head Jan wore a broad-brimmed hat with a flowing feather. Behind him rode his splendid soldiers. The body-guard of the town beat the drum enthusiastically, and the Cologne people called out: "Long live our Jan van Werth!"

When the celebrated general passed the gate, he stopped his horse just in front of Griet's apple baskets, and looking down upon the old wrinkled woman, met her questioning glance with an odd smile. "Ah Griet," said he slowly, "whoever would have thought it?" At the sound of his voice an expression of sudden recognition passed over her worn features, and she muttered sorrowfully, but still audibly to the proud rider, "Oh, Jan, if I had only known it!"

A magnificent monument in the form of the statue of Jan van Werth now stands in the centre of the old market of Cologne.

It was erected there in memory not only of the heroic deeds of the brave general, but also as a warning to all Cologne maidens not to reject their suitors because they are poor, for one day, like Jan van Werth, they may become famous, and then they will not, like Griet, have to sigh over things that "might have been."

Xanten

SIEGFRIED

Siegfried, — and as we pronounce this glorious name, the hero looks forth at us with shining eyes, for was not Siegfried the perfect embodiment of all that was beautiful and good?

For centuries stories have been told and poems have been sung of the bold adventures of the young hero, whose energy only found satisfaction in victorious fights.

The original name of the small town on the lower Rhine now called Xanten, was "Ad Santos," „peace for the saints." It was thus named on account of the pious warriors of the Theban legion who in the fourth century had boldly died there for their creed under their leader, Victor.

At the time to which our story refers, a mighty stronghold formed the centre of the little town Xanten. A king called Siegmund with his wife Siegelinde and their son Siegfried lived there.

While a mere boy, Siegfried had already a kingly stature, and an almost untamable diposition of mind. When he was only thirteen years of age, his longing for grand deeds was so great that he found it impossible to remain inactive at home. From old songs and legends which the minstrels recited in his father's castle, he had heard so much of bold adventures and brilliant exploits performed by his forefathers, that he was most anxious to follow in their steps. He felt strong and valiant enough to undertake like the heroes of old, dangerous journeys. Therefore young Siegfried left one day his ancestral halls, and wandered southwards along the clear blue river. He soon found an opportunity of testing his courage.

At the foot of the Seven Mountains lived a celebrated armourer called Mimer, renowned for making excellent swords. Our hero liked this warlike trade, and he asked the master to receive him as an apprentice, that he might learn the praiseworthy art of forging a good sword for himself. The armourer agreed, and Siegfried remained at Mimer's workshop. The journeymen with whom the youth had to work, soon learned the enormous strength of their new companion. The boy, often not knowing how to give expression to his desire for action, would take up his fellow-workmen, lift them high into the air, and

drop them, not always softly to the ground. Or when his anger was roused, he would imprint black and blue marks on their backs with his strong fists. Once he even smashed with one stroke of his hammer all the iron bars in the armoury, and knocked the anvil into the ground with a mighty blow.

Mimer looked on with dismay, amazed at the boy's almost supernatural strength, but fearing that Siegfried's wrath might some time turn against him, he thought to rid himself of his dangerous apprentice, and conceived a cunning plan to kill him. A horrible dragon lived in the neighbouring forest, which tore every wanderer to pieces who chanced to cross its way. Mimer ordered Siegfried to fetch a sack from the charcoal-burner in that forest, well knowing that the boy would never return thence.

The youth, without knowing the danger he was about to meet, went cheerfully on his way. In the middle of the thick wood he kindled a charcoal-kiln, and amused himself by putting big burning branches and young trees into the fire.

Suddenly the monster came swiftly creeping on its huge claws. Curving its shimmering body the ugly beast opened wide its jaws to devour the young charcoal-burner. Siegfried's eyes brightened up at the prospect of an encounter with the terrible animal before him. Without a moment's hesitation, he tore a flaming beam out of the kiln, and pushed its burning end deep into the open mouth of the dragon. Roaring with pain the monster turned round beating violently with its prickly tail, trying in its agony to crush Siegfried. But he, jumping skilfully aside, rapidly dealt it heavy blows, and succeeded at last in smashing its head with a large piece of rock. He severed the head from the body, and threw it into the blazing flames. To his astonishment he observed how a stream of grease gushed from the burning pile, and collected in a pool at his feet.

Close by the charcoal-kiln stood an old lime-tree. A little bird sang merrily in its branches. Siegfried, involuntarily listening to the clear strain, made out the following words: "If you would be covered with horn, and become invulnerable, undress yourself and plunge into the pool."

Siegfried quickly threw his clothes off and anointed his whole body with the dragon's grease. While thus occupied a leaf from the old lime-tree above dropped between his shoulders. This part of the hero's body remained without horn. When he had finished, he took up the monster's head and returned to Mimer's workshop. The nearer he got to the smithy, the more his rage against his wicked master increased. Mimer had seen the boy from afar approaching with the trophy of his fight, and had hidden in great fear.

Siegfried however soon found him out and slew him on the spot. Then he forged a good two edged sword and shining armour for himself, and having saddled the best horse of Mimer's stable, he left the smithy to look for new adventures.

For a long time he travelled aimlessly about, saw mountains and valleys, rivers and lakes, cities and hamlets, until he at last arrived at the seashore. He embarked with his good horse, and was cast by a gale on the rocky coast of an unknown country. The noble animal climbed courageously up the stony beach, and carried its rider to an enchanted castle which was surrounded by a wall of flames. For a moment Siegfried stood irresolute. Suddenly the voice of the little bird sounded again above him, "Break the charm. Straight into the flames with a bold dash. A most lovely maiden will be thy reward."

The youth took courage, spurred his steed, and with a plunge horse and rider disappeared in the flames, which were at once extinguished. The charm was broken. Before him lay a wonderful castle. Siegfried penetrated into its interior, and was amazed to find every living creature in a profound sleep within; the horses in their stalls, the grooms in the stables, the cook at the hearth. When he entered the high hall a lovely scene presented itself to his view. On a couch the most exquisite form of a woman lay sleeping. Her golden hair was strewn with precious stones, and her limbs were clothed in the most costly garments.

The young hero looked for a while, lost in admiration. Then bending down to her, he pressed a passionate kiss on her rosy lips. Brunhilde, the fair sleeper, opened her eyes, and at the same time every living being in the castle awoke.

The old legend depicts in glowing colours the sweet hours of love that followed for Siegfried and Brunhilde. Days and months passed by without the lovers being aware of it. However fond of adventures Siegfried was, he felt himself chained to the spot by her subtle charms. While thus undecided he heard one day the bird's voice: "Leave the castle and give up a life of ignoble leisure; direct your steps towards the country of the Nibelungen, take possession of their immense treasures and of the precious invisible cap."

At the prospect of new adventures Siegfried could not be kept back any longer by Brunhilde. They parted with the solemn promise of meeting again.

A great many exploits are recorded of the proud hero which he performed in the country of the Nibelungen. After a long and hard struggle with the cunning dwarfs, he took away with him their treasure, as well as the cap which had the gift of making its wearer invisible.

Years had passed by, and Siegfried longed to see the place of his childhood again. So he turned homewards and reached Xanten after many adventures. The joy of his noble parents at seeing their valiant son again was indescribable.

The legend of Siegfried's youthful exploits and his home-coming is full of romance and happiness. But if we listen to the continuation of his story we shall find how every human feeling has its place in the hero's biography, great joy, deep sorrow, passionate love, glowing hatred, heroism and perfidy, cowardice and high courage, until at last the legend of Siegfried ends in a pitiful wail of grief.

LOHENGRIN

The weathercock on the ancient stronghold at Cleves is a swan, and in olden times the dynasty that ruled over the lovely country round Cleves had also a swan in their crest. A legend, tragic and beautiful, preserved to posterity forever in Richard Wagner's lovely opera, is connected with it, — the legend of Lohengrin.

Long centuries ago deep sorrow brooded over the walls of the castle at Cleves. Its mistress, the Duchess Elsa was in great distress. Her beloved husband had died, and his remains had been brought to their last resting-place. As soon as the tomb had closed over them, one of the late Duke's vassals, Telramund, rose in revolt, aud imperiously claimed the right to reign over the dukedom. The audacious man went so far as to ask the widowed Duchess to become his wife, declaring that this was the only means of saving her rank, which the death of her husband had deprived her of.

271

Elsa, the youthful and lovely mistress, implored the knights of her dominion to assist her in her trouble, and to take up arms against the rebel. But Telramund, little disconcerted by this appeal, offered to fight in single combat with anybody who dared to take up the quarrel with him, well knowing that, on account of his immense strength, nobody would dare to become his adversary.

The days passed in deepest sorrow for the unfortunate Duchess. The moment was approaching when the rebel would make bold to proclaim openly his claims before the whole assembled nobility on the open space before the castle. The fatal hour came. Pale, her face covered by her widow's veil, her queenly form enveloped in mourning garments, Elsa descended from her castle to the assembly. The large plain was crowded with a throng of people, and glittered with the brilliant armour of the kinghts.

The unfaithful vassal, covered from head to foot in shining armour, came forward with bold steps and claimed in a loud voice the hand and dominion of the Duchess. The knights around, deluded by his valiant appearance and the firmness of his voice, broke into loud applause. Some of the crowd joined them in their cry of approbation, but most of the people looked on, full of pity and admiration for their youthful mistress.

No answer to his first challenge having come, Telramund repeated his audacious demand, offering again to fight in single combat anybody who dared to accept it. His eyes glanced defiantly over the brilliant multitude of knights. He perceived with triumphant joy, how they all shrank from fighting with him. — Elsa looked still paler than before.

For a third time the challenge of Telramund was heard. It sounded clearly over the whole plain. But none of the bright warriors came forward to take up the combat for Elsa's sake.

On the contrary deep silence followed the third challenge, and everybody's eyes were fixed on the forsaken princess who looked in her abandoned position still more lovely. The little hope that had till that moment given her strength to bear her misfortune, had now entirely vanished. In her utter desolation she offered a fervent prayer to heaven. On her rosary, so the legend records, a little silver bell was hanging, which possessed the wonderful gift of giving forth, whenever slightly touched, a clear ringing sound audible even at a great distance. In praying to God for deliverance from her great trouble, she pressed the cross on her rosary fervently to her lips. The silver bell tinkled, and at the same moment a little barge suddenly appeared on the blue river. When it came nearer, everybody looked with astonishment at the strange vessel. Its form was light and graceful; but what astonished the people most was that it was not moved by either oar or rudder, but was gently gliding on the blue waves drawn by a snow-white swan. In the middle of the vessel stood a knight in shining silver armour.

Long golden locks emerged from under his glittering helmet, his bright blue eyes looked boldly over the crowd on the shore, and his hand held the hilt of his broadsword firmly.

The strange boat stopped just opposite the plain where the people stood motionless with amazement. The knight landed from the barge, giving a sign with his hand to the swan, which swam gently down the Rhine.

In silence and awe the multitude made room for the stranger who approached with firm steps toward the middle of the brilliant circle, and saluted the assembly with a solemn grace. Then he bent his knees before the Duchess and rising, turned towards Telramund, challenging him proudly to fight with him for the hand and dominion of Elsa of Brabant. The bold rebel's temerity seemed to fail him for a few moments,

but gathering fresh courage he pulled his sword from its sheath with a loud scornful laugh.

The next moment the two knights darted at each other, their blades clashing in rapid strokes.

The whole crowd looked with wonder and amazement at the strange knight's great prowess. He parried the blows of his strong adversary skilfully. The combat lasted for some time, and neither of the fighters seemed to give way. Suddenly a subdued cry was heard, and at the same time the presumptuous vassal sank to the ground, pierced by the sword of him whom God had sent, and expired. A tremendous shout of joy burst from the gazing crowd, which rang from one end of the plain to the other and was echoed by the glittering waves of the Rhine. The people rejoiced in the victory, and thought that God himself had decided the combat in favour of Elsa.

The Duchess felt greatly moved. In her overflowing gratitude she sank down before her deliverer with tears in her eyes. But he bade her rise, and bowing low before her asked her to become his wife. She consented. What a heaven of bliss opened for the Duchess of Brabant! All her former troubles were forgotten.

Her gratitude towards her rescues was transformed into passionate love, to which Lohengrin, the virtuous knight, responded with tender adoration.

Yet though everything seemed now so serene in the life of the Duchess, there was a dim cloud which threatened to darken the clear prospect of her happiness. On their wedding-day Elsa had to promise her bridegroom that she would never inquire about his name, his home, or his descent.

Trusting her deliverer's honour and chivalrous bearing, she took the strange oath without a moment's hesitation.

Many years of bliss and happiness passed, and Elsa of Brabant had strictly kept the promise she had made on her bridal morning. Their happiness was still more enhanced by the birth of three boys of great promise. They were their parents' joy, and bade fair to become in future shining ornaments of knighthood.

It happened however, when the eyes of the Duchess were resting with pride on her sons, that her mother's heart thought with grief of the sollemn oath she had sworn on her wedding-day.

With how much more pride would she have looked upon her sons if she could have known them to be the offspring of a high and noble race. She did not doubt however that her beloved husband's lineage. was a most noble one.

Yet the thought that his sons might never bear their father's name, nor be able to add new glories to it, was lying heavily on her mind, and darkened the radiant image of her husband, that like a deity filled her whole soul.

The fatal question she had for so long withheld burst one day forcibly from her lips.

When she had pronounced the awful words the proud hero grew pale, and freeing himself softly from her tender embrace, he cried out in bitter grief: "Woe to thee, my beloved wife and woe also to me! Now that thou hast uttered the question thou didst swear solemnly never to ask, our happiness is gone for ever. I must part from thee, never to see thee again."

A cry of anguish rose from her lips, but she was unable to keep him back. Waving his hand to her in a mute farewell her noble husband left the castle. He went to the Rhine and blew his silver horn.

Its sound was echoed from the shore like a long sob. The white swan with the boat soon appeared gliding gently over the river.

Lohengrin stepped into the boat and soon vanished out of sight and was seen no more.

His unhappy wife was inconsolable. Her grief was so intense that a short time after her health gave way, and she sank into a premature grave.

Her sons became the founders of a noble and distinguished race in the Rhenish country. Their crest is a swan.

The traveller who visits Cleves will still find a tombstone in its church with a knight carved on it, and a swan sitting at his feet.

Zuider Zee

STAVOREN

A strange story is still told about the city of Stavoren on the Zuider Zee. It was a wondrous town, but like Vineta on the Baltic Sea it vanished from the earth.

The merchants of Stavoren were the rulers of the Ocean, and the treasures of all known countries were lying in their port. The houses were lovely palaces, furnished in their interior like the marvellous abodes of the Sultan Haroun Al Rachid, in the "Arabian Nights".

Of all the wealthy people of the town, there was nobody so much blessed with riches as Richberta, a pround and beautiful lady. Smiling fortune had lavishly poured its gifts upon her, and threw fresh treasures daily at her feet. She seemed to own everything beautiful that this life can bestow, but one thing she did not possess, and that was the soft fire of woman's kindness which lightens and warms the soul, and throws on all its surroundings a mild reflecting gleam. Richberta was cold and indifferent to both the pleasures and the sorrows of her fellow-men. When night casts her shades upon the earth, all the sweet bright birds and butterflies hide and make room for a host of ghastly animals like owls and bats. So in Richberta's soul all her soft qualities had gone to sleep for want of the tender gleam of love, and only dark and harsh feelings haunted her soul. Immense pride in her own wealth, a bitter envy towards those who possessed more than she did, were her ruling passions.

Once Richberta gave a grand feast. While the luxurious meal was being served, a stranger entered who had come from far away to see the wonders of Stavoren with his own eyes. "I have seen" said he, bowing low to the lovely hostess, "many countries and many a princely court, but I confess that Stavoren surpasses them all in splendour."

Highly flattered the proud lady bade him welcome to her table. According to the customs of the Orient whence he came, he begged for some bread and salt. Richberta ordered her servants to bring both, but it was useless to look for such simple fare in her house where only the most luxurious food was to be had.

Without making any remarks however the stranger sat down and partook of the costly dishes. Then he began to relate his journeys, his success and his failures in life, and dwelt with great eloquence on the instability of earthly fortunes. All the guests listened with interest to what he said. Only Richberta sat gloomily at the head of her table. She felt angry that the stranger dared in her very presence to find fault with wealth and splendour, and to predict its probable destruction. Moreover she thought it rude in him that he had no word of praise for her own brilliant beauty, nor a glance of astonishment for her gorgeous palace. Her offended vanity induced her at last to force from him the praise he so obstinately withheld. "O, gracious Lady," said he rather reluctantly, "marvellous indeed is your home and fit for a queen. If you travelled far and near, you could not find its equal. But, my lady, among your treasures I miss one thing, and that is the noblest that the earth produces."

Richberta was very anxious to learn what it was, that she might get it, and entreated her guest to name the precious thing. But he avoided any direct answer to her impetuous questions, and soon afterwards took his leave on a slight pretext.

———

On the open sea, a proud fleet was sailing. Its commander, strange to say, did not himself know the aim of his journey. His mistress Richberta of Stavoren, had directed him to travel to all parts of the world to find out and bring home the most costly treasure.

According to her command he set out, cruised the ocean to the East, and to the West, and searched everywhere for the unknown gift.

In doing so it happened one day that sea-water spoiled a part of the provisions of one of the ships. It was the flour and bread, the want of which was keenly felt by the whole crew. In this necessity the captain saw clearly that neither gold nor pearls could outweigh the value of bread, and the meaning of the mysterious words the stranger from the Orient had spoken to Richberta, dawned upon him.

He steered to the coast and took a large cargo of the finest wheat aboard his ships. Full of joy at having at last found what he deemed the most costly thing on earth, he sailed towards Stavoren, where he arrived safely.

When Richberta learned of the common merchandise her captain had brought home, she summoned him before her and asked him contemptuously: "On which side of the vessel has the cargo of corn been taken in?" "On the right, mistress," answered the faithful servant, doubtful of what she meant. "Then," continued she coldly, "throw it from the left into the sea again."

———

The day after the return of the fleet an animated scene was witnessed in the port of Stavoren.

The numerous poor people of the town on hearing of the wicked command of Richberta, had come to beg of her not to spoil the precious wheat, but to divide it among those who were so much in want of it.

The proud lady appeared herself to see that her command was executed. It was a touching spectacle to see how the crowd of miserable women and children surrounded the noble lady in her costly garments. The sight of so much misery would have moved many a cold heart, but Richberta showed no pity. She moved forward impatiently as if she heard not the supplications. But the crowd of women stopped her. They fell on their knees and entreated her with uplifted hands and tears in their eyes for the preservation of God's precious gift. Richberta heard but remained unrelenting. Her command was fulfilled, and the golden wheat was thrown into the sea.

A storm of reproaches rose from the poor on the shore, and many a mother prayed to God on her knees to avenge this wickedness.

The curses of the hungry people were fulfilled, far sooner than they expected.

In the same year innumerable earless blades of wheat rose from the bottom of the sea like a forest, catching up mud, mire, weed, and remains of animals, so that by and by a dune rose under water which stopped the ships from entering the port of Stavoren.

The inhabitants of the town who had principally lived by commerce, suddenly found the source of their wealth stopped. Want and poverty took possion of the once rich city. Richberta, whom everybody recognised as the author of this misfortune, lost everything in the general impoverishment, and was driven by the enraged populace from the town. The once proud and rich lady had now to beg for her bread. She walked wearily from village to village, curses following her wherever she went. She died in utter destitution.

The sea that had for so many years been the blessing of Stavoren was now the destruction of the voluptuous city. One night it rose with immense power against the dunes, burst

285

throught them, and flooding the town with huge waves, buried it forever.

To this day, the fishermen on the Zuider Zee relate the story of the wonderful sunken city that once towered high into the air. When the water is clear they imagine they can see the high steeples of Stavoren's churches and the towers of her palaces shimmering up from the bottom of the sea.

CONTENTS